The
Treachery
at
Nether Stowey

The
Treachery
at
Nether Stowey

Matthew Greenwood

First published in Great Britain by The Blue Shed Press 2011

Reprinted 2012

This is a work of fiction. The scenario outlined is entirely the product of the author's imagination.

Front cover: Tintern Abbey from the Ferry by J.S. Prout (1838) reproduced by permission of Llyfrgell Genedlaethol Cymru / The National Library of Wales

William White's 1797 map of Somerset reproduced by permission of Somerset Archives and Local Studies Service: Ref. D\RA/9/24

ISBN 978-0-9569886-0-7

Prepared and pri[nted by]

York Publishing S[ervices]
64 Hallfield Road
Layerthorpe
York
YO31 7ZQ

Tel: 01904 431213

www.yps-publish[ing]

For Hannah

"This beautiful fabric of Love the system of Spies & Informers has shaken to the very foundation. There have been multiplied among us 'Men who carry tales to shed blood!'"

Samuel Taylor Coleridge, Lectures, 1795

***

"Much of its tone is matter-of-fact, informative, even slightly technical, as if Coleridge was anxious … to get his measurements right."

George Watson on 'Kubla Khan'

Historical Foreword

When war broke out between Britain and France in 1793, the British Government moved swiftly and ruthlessly to silence a domestic opposition it perceived to be in league with the enemy. It enacted a raft of repressive legislation and activated a network of spies, informants and *agents provocateurs*.

In 1794, three leading members of the London Corresponding Society, a prominent network of radicals, were arrested and charged with treason. When their trials collapsed, the Government set about re-drafting the treason statutes to ensure this would not happen again. Four other men tried for sedition at this time were not so lucky. All were found guilty and transported to Botany Bay: only one of them lived to return.

The action of this novel begins on Thursday 21st September 1797. At this date, peace negotiations between Britain and France had irretrievably broken down. With the capitulation of Austria, its final ally on the continent, Britain stood alone. The rising star of the French army, Napoleon Bonaparte, was manoeuvring his forces into position across the English Channel.

To most people, a maritime invasion seemed only a matter of time.

Dramatis Personae

London

THE DUKE OF PORTLAND, Home Secretary
JOHN KING, Permanent Under-Secretary at the Home Office
GEORGE HEATON, a Government Spy
WILLIAM PITT THE YOUNGER, Prime Minister
MADDISON, a Government Code-Breaker
Sundry members of the Privy Council

Nether Stowey

WILLIAM WORDSWORTH, tenant of Alfoxton House
MISS WORDSWORTH, his sister
THOMAS POOLE, a wealthy tanner
SAMUEL COLERIDGE, his secretary
CHRISTOPHER TRICKIE, keeper of the Dog Pound

Edinburgh

DANIEL WALLACE, a watch-maker
THOMAS LENNOX, a troublesome person

WALES

BRISTOL

Culver Sand

Bridg

Ba

PORLOCK · MINEHEAD

Exmoor Forest · DUNSTER · WATCHET

NETH
ST

River

DULVERTON

WIVELISCOMBE

MILVERTON

WELLINGT

Bla

D
E
V
O
N

Rich grazing and dairy Lands
near Bridgwater Axbridge &c

Meadow Pasture and Arable intermixt
in high cultivation

Turf Bog capable of
little improvement

Mountainous Lands
interspersed with
fertile Vales

Coals in general the
Surface similar to the
adjacent Lands

SOMERSET,

for the

AGRICULTURAL SURVEY

taken by Jno. Billingsley;

Sketched by Wm. White, 1797.

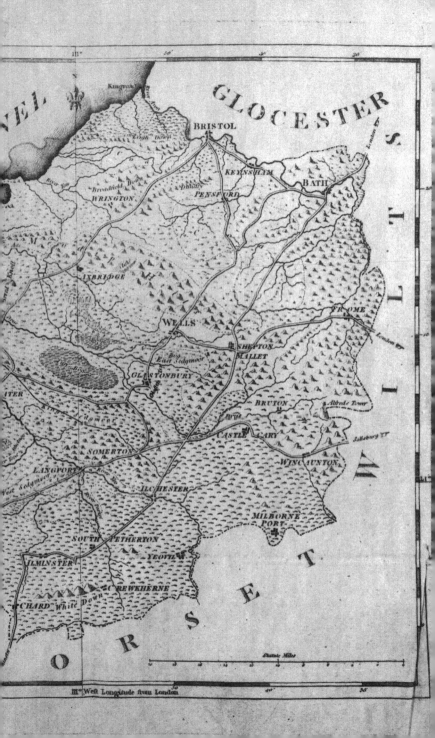

Part One

Fears in Solitude

"In times like this it behoves us to be on our guard, and there is a maxim which it is always sage to bear in mind, namely, that nothing can happen which the government of a country should consider as a trifle."

William Henry Cavendish Bentinck,
Third Duke of Portland,
Home Secretary, 1794-1801

Memorandum from the Duke of Portland to Permanent Under-Secretaries at the Home Office, Thursday 21st September 1797

Earlier today the Cabinet met to consider the recent *coup d'état* in Paris and weigh its consequences for the conduct of British foreign and domestic policy. There was unanimous agreement that we cannot now hope to negotiate a cessation of hostilities on terms remotely acceptable to us. The nation is to be readied for an assault by substantial French forces early in the new year, most likely along the coastlines of Kent, Sussex or Essex.

Never has there been a greater call for vigilance within our own shores. All reports of unusual or suspicious activity, especially in coastal areas, however trifling, ought to be the subject of extremely close scrutiny. Careful attention should be paid to the whereabouts and behaviour of those radicals, dissenters and foreign nationals who have previously been identified as a threat, or otherwise demonstrated sympathy with the French cause.

I urge you not to confine your attention to those places already mentioned. You need hardly be reminded that the French attack on the Bristol Channel last February, and the subsequent landing in Wales, caused a run on the banks.

I must also demand a full assessment of all information received by this office in the months prior to the French landing. You are to concern yourselves with any sign, however obscure, that may have alerted us to the prospect of an enemy assault.

Memorandum from John King, Permanent Under-Secretary at the Home Office, to the Duke of Portland, Friday 22nd September 1797

Your Grace may recall the investigation undertaken last month by one of our agents into a set of violent democrats assembled in the neighbourhood of Nether Stowey, Somerset; a place which, as your Grace would wish to know, is but a few hours from Bristol and no more than a short walk from the sea.

One of these men, Mr Wordsworth, had taken possession of a large property named Alfoxton House. He was observed by one Mr Christopher Trickie of the Dog Pound, Alfoxton, to be escorting visitors on strange excursions about the local country by day and night, all the time entering observations in a secret portfolio. One of these visitors had inquired of Mr Trickie whether the brook passing his residence was navigable as far down as the sea. It might be added that Mr Wordsworth has no wife, but is accompanied by a woman who passes for his sister.

Our agent found that Mr Wordsworth's rent was guaranteed by a local tanner, one Thomas Poole, who has established a Poor Man's Club in Nether Stowey and placed himself at its head, thereby assuming command of more than 150 men. He has also secured accommodations for a Mr Coldridge from Bristol, a man reckoned to be of superior ability and thought to be in possession of a printing press.

The strange nature of these men's conduct and the precise neighbourhood in which they have chosen to settle give much cause for concern, especially now all prospect of peace is at an end. I would respectfully propose that a second agent be despatched with the utmost celerity to establish beyond any doubt the true nature of their ambitions.

NB – I should note that this Office received information concerning a most suspicious person who was frequently sighted making observations of the countryside about Fishguard not six months prior to the French attack close by that place. However, the information was not acted upon by local magistrates, despite Your Grace's written instruction to the contrary.

Memorandum from the Duke of Portland to John King, Saturday 23rd September 1797

This affair at Nether Stowey is exactly the sort of thing I fear.

Without doubt you must despatch another agent to Somerset. Choose this man carefully. He must be terrier as well as bloodhound. Impress upon him most gravely the requirement for hard evidence; letters, coded papers, etc. We cannot be left to rely on the inconsequential prattling of rustics.

He ought to be in no doubt of the advantage that shall accrue if his sojourn results in an example of the solemn fate which most certainly awaits all those who make the destruction of this country their foul & treacherous object.

PS – Were any of these men ever in France?

Memorandum from John King to the Duke of Portland, Monday 25th September 1797

I hereby confirm that an agent has been despatched to Nether Stowey.

This man is indeed terrier as well as bloodhound; unyielding in his beliefs & possessed of a fierce intolerance of the French, which is rivalled only by his detestation of those who would conspire with them.

He has formerly exhibited much prowess in securing the kind of information we seek. He is under no illusion what is at stake in this matter; nor of the great advantage to be had from it. I might add that he is blessed with a most pleasing capacity for subterfuge and an excellent ability to disguise his accent and gait.

There is little doubt we shall soon discover from him whether these men harbour diabolical ambitions, and, if so, what is the readiness of the Poor Man's Army.

**Extract from the 'Gentleman's Magazine',
September 1797**

A few days ago, two large porpoises came up the river as high as London Bridge. Yesterday one of the same species made its appearance nearly in the same quarter and kept sporting about during the heavy rain. It has been generally understood such appearances indicate a hard and severe winter.

Extracts from the Notebooks of George Heaton
(Subsequently Deciphered)

Set out from London in a pestilential mist.

Once this dispersed, only source of distraction a fellow traveller who treated all present to tirade against recent tax rises. Declared himself fierce opponent of higher duty on spirits, tea & sugar. Expressed vehement displeasure at new tax on legacies & doubling of levy on horses kept for pleasure.

Became clear he set too low a price on value of liberty.

Determined to report him as soon as we reached Bath.

***

Thomas Poole – manufacturer of leather – the village Robespierre?

Coldridge – reckoned clever – kept as amanuensis?

Wordsworth – damnable hypocrite – revelling in time as lord of manor & lisping in French to mistress he would have us believe his sister?

***

Arrived at inn – Castle of Comfort – between Nether Stowey & village of Holford. Suits purpose well enough.

Supped on dish of game & cider. Decided to try opinions of landlord by referring to abominable events of July

'89. Response more vehement than could have hoped. Conversations halted abruptly; blood drained from host's face. Steadied himself for a moment, then looked me in eye & declared he would never forget what happened that month; "no, nor could he forgive it neither".

Congratulated myself upon finding lodgings beneath roof of true patriot.

***

Fell into conversation with man who works at Stowey copper mine.

Landlord's niece murdered July '89 by local charcoal burner whom she had married a few weeks previous. Villain loved some other woman. Hanged the following month & body placed in iron cage to swing facing cottage of his parents. Remained there one year before it fell to ground in storm. Place named after this: Walford's gibbet.

Cannot but observe salutary example of English justice made manifest.

Extract from the Journal of the Duke of Portland, Monday 2nd October 1797

I am not a little perturbed to discover that a growth or blemish on my cheek, which the doctors call a cyst, must be cut away at the earliest opportunity, if merely for the sake of precaution. I have been warned the operation will be painful in the extreme and my hands must be tied back to restrain me. None the less, if all go well, the threat to my health shall be expunged in one swift action. The scar left behind shall barely denote it existed.

I have sought reassurance on this procedure from the Surgeon Extraordinary to His Majesty the King, and was informed the Prime Minister himself underwent something very similar little more than a decade ago. At that time, he was most insistent neither his hands be tied back, nor the rest of his body secured. When I asked Mr Pitt of this, he told me, without so much as a trace of a smile, that it was early in his ministry and he was afraid the surgeon would step back to reveal the leaders of the opposition, newly sharpened blades in hand.

He avers there are no lasting ill-effects, the pain was not unendurable, and as a method of subjecting the head of an aristocrat to a blade he prefers it to that most lately favoured in Paris; an opinion with which I can scarcely disagree.

Extracts from the Notebooks of George Heaton
(Subsequently Deciphered)

Tenant of Alfoxton as strange as he is suspicious.

Twice now seen him emerge from house with vexed expression, pace up & down muttering to himself, then moment of intense joy & hastens back inside.

Some say he is conjuror or alchemist; others that he distils heady brews.

Gaunt man, upward of thirty, with cropped hair & high forehead.

Vertical furrow on right cheek. Duelling scar?

Narrow across chest with dropping shoulders & rolling gait. To disguise military bearing?

Clothes most suspicious: brown fustian jacket & striped pantaloons not worthy of house he occupies.

Woman with him is younger. Little sign of family resemblance. Passes most of time on north side of house. Tenant works at desk in library, then they both walk out to find isolated spots. Small child with them roams free like savage.

Why such large house when manner of living so modest?

Why not otherwise engaged in time of national peril?

Why so aloof?

***

Alfoxton House faces south toward a high hill populated with trees and dense fern providing much cover. Two storeys tall, with seven upstairs windows at front & three either side of main entrance below. Two gabled windows in attic.

Park contains sufficient deer to feed a small army of troop for several days. Bountiful supply of water from the brooks & streams running down off the hills. Fuel for camp-fires from the woods & dells.

House must contain at least three large parlours & ten lodging rooms which would offer excellent accommodations to officers of enemy landing party.

To north, commanding views of coast across meadows & pasture to anyone possessing the most elementary spyglass.

NB – Last occupant local rector, Lancelot St Albyn. Died six or seven years ago. Great-nephew will inherit when comes of age.

***

Attended St Albyn family bailiff: Mr J Bartholomew of Putsham. Told him am agent in employ of eminent personage desirous to secure Alfoxton at first opportunity. Willing to pay double rent of existing tenants.

Consulted documents re. possibility of evicting them before midsummer next. Found to be impossible.

Ruse paid off. Close look at legal papers.

Tenant <u>William</u> Wordsworth formerly of Racedown Lodge, nr Lyme Regis.

Rent £24 p.a. guaranteed by Thomas Poole who drew up & witnessed himself. Signed & dated *14th July* …

***

Some mistake. Name not Coldridge – COL<u>E</u>RIDGE.

Wild unkempt appearance with large grey eyes & bad teeth. Clothes often dirty. Longish, rough, black mane like unbroken colt.

Wild extravagance in financial matters. Coal bill unpaid. Owes money to servant-girl, shoe-maker & chandler. Local woman with whom he has danced – not wife – terms him opinionated, talking everybody down, fatiguing to listen to.

Light beyond midnight on coldest of evenings. Seeks solace in printing press more than wife of two years? Told he regularly consults Poole's large book collection; must know more of this.

Cottage situated at far end of Lime St. Nothing between it & open hills. Well-placed to steal away to clandestine meetings. Back door gives out onto long narrow strip of kitchen-garden, small orchard & passage leading directly to Poole's garden via stinking tan-yard. Easy for two men to commune without recourse to public thoroughfare.

Have seen them do this.

***

Poole a stout, plain-looking bachelor possessing little in way of own hair.

Habit of supporting reckless young men? Coleridge merely latest?

Lives with invalid mother & dun mongrel whelp.

Have it on good authority he gave local cabinet-maker *Rights of Man* & intervened most strenuously to stop burning of T. Paine in effigy. Regarded by labourers, cloth-workers & quarrymen as village statesman. Frequently called upon to act as arbiter in their disputes. Named guardian of several children. (More to this?)

NB – Radical opinions greatly embarrassing to nearby relations; one of whom clergyman & Fellow of Oxford college.

***

Drills & manoeuvres of Poor Man's Army?

Where store of weapons concealed? Poole's tannery? House or woods at Alfoxton? Outhouse in Coleridge's garden – patrolled by large & aggressive pig?

Memorandum from John King to the Duke of Portland, Monday 9th October 1797

I trust this despatch reaches Your Grace in an improved condition.

It is now established beyond all doubt that Alfoxton House possesses manifold attractions as a staging post for an enemy invasion force. The tenant, William Wordsworth, holds himself aloof from the local people, the better to pursue his clandestine activities. And it would appear from a county map that he has formerly inhabited other large properties enjoying ready prospect of the nation's coastline.

The wealthy tanner, Thomas Poole, exerts great sway over the local poor men. He has been seen to engage in suspicious assignations with his secretary, whose true name is Coleridge, via a private passage to the rear of their dwellings.

Upon learning the secretary's true identity, I have instituted numerous inquiries both at Bristol, from whence he is rumoured to come, and at the universities. I have also ordered an urgent investigation of the property last inhabited by Mr Wordsworth and the particular area of coastline visible from it.

Urgent priority is now given to searching out evidence against these men, whether it be the observations they made of the coast at the beginning of August, or the traitorous communications they are conceived to have entered into with the French.

I trust this manner of proceeding is to Your Grace's satisfaction.

Record of a Conversation between the Prime Minister & the Home Secretary, Tuesday 10th October 1797

The HOME SECRETARY commenced by stating he had good reason to fear the French were again conniving at our coasts, aided and abetted by traitorous elements within these shores: the London Corresponding Society, the United Scotsmen, various Catholic conspirators, etc.

The PRIME MINISTER said he was not surprised to hear this, but he placed great faith in the belief such attacks could be disrupted or, in the last resort, repelled. The most able and skilful officers, both Naval and Military, were presently engaged in drawing up a formidable plan for the defence of the country.

The HOME SECRETARY suggested that, as a precaution, all persons situated within ten miles of vulnerable coastline should be required to conduct an inventory of crops and livestock, with a view to destroying these in the event of a forced withdrawal.

The PRIME MINISTER agreed this ought to be done, but said he hoped matters would never reach such a desperate pass, taking into account the strength of the navy, the vigilance of the public, and the array of legislation now at the Government's disposal.

The HOME SECRETARY said he was afraid the imminent discovery of certain plots must reveal the threat was by no means annihilated with the surrender of Colonel

Tate's *Legion Noir* in Wales last February. It was his grave concern that present resources were insufficient to deal with the problem. Maintaining a network of spies and informants was proving a severe drain on budgets; there was already a backlog of copied mail awaiting the attention of code breakers, etc.

The PRIME MINISTER intimated that the discovery of such plots might well suggest the adequacy of resources rather than its reverse. But he had always been of the opinion there was no merit in saving money only for it to be plundered by the French. This brought him to the matter of the proposed evacuation of the nation's gold bullion from the Bank of England to a secret location in the event of an enemy

[Page or pages missing]

The PRIME MINISTER observed that, at the current rate of expenditure, he might yet be able to carry out the evacuation himself, bearing what remained of the nation's wealth from the capital in his handkerchief.

The HOME SECRETARY said he could not allow himself to be dissuaded by frivolity from reiterating in the most urgent terms the grave threat posed by traitorous elements within these shores. He must praise the work of his department, especially the Alien Office, which was being carried out under very greatly straitened circumstances. It was his duty to enquire if it were not the height of folly to expect him to oversee the security of the nation with a staff that numbered twenty-six only when the chamber-keeper was taken into account.

The PRIME MINISTER said he hoped he should not be accused of underestimating the scale of the threat. Nothing would give him greater pleasure than to accede to this request. But it must be remembered that the nation's finances were subject to many competing demands at this time of peril, not least keeping the army in victual and the navy afloat, as recent mutinies had demonstrated. It would not be right to make a decision at this moment.

Letter from John King to George Heaton, Wednesday 11th October 1797

Sir

I have considered the contents of your letter which you did right to ensure reached me with all possible speed. I hereby acknowledge the extra expense incurred in your chartering a small vessel to carry it as far as Bristol and, in the process, to undertake certain observations of the coast. By way of reimbursement, I transmit one half of a bank note; the other to follow under separate cover as is the accustomed procedure.

I should, of course, declare myself satisfied with your report so far as it goes. I shall make prompt use of the descriptions with which you have furnished us. And you may be assured His Grace has been informed of your fears as to these men's probable intentions.

None the less, I would remind you of the particular discussion which took place between us prior to your departure from London & the undertakings entered into at that time. You are to be in no doubt as to the high value His Grace places on the possession of compelling evidence.

To advance your present inquiries, I suggest you pay especial attention to the following matters:

i.   Is any of these men, or any of the persons with whom they have chosen to associate, in possession of a Box or Chest which is treated with the utmost circumspection & guarded most jealously?

ii. Could any of them have entered into a treacherous communication with the enemy? If so, by what means?

I note your assertion that Poole's amanuensis appears to represent the weak link in this conspiracy. If so, I need hardly advise you further how to proceed.

Extracts from the Notebooks of George Heaton
(Subsequently Deciphered)

Witness to secret meeting at which things said as dangerous as anything heard in all my time fulfilling duties of loyal subject. If I should fail, these people will surely plunge nation into anarchy & terror. Villages burned to ground & crops scattered to wind; men impaled on pike-staffs & womenfolk violated.

***

Set out for cottage of Christopher Trickie, aka Dog Pound, in garb of labouring man fallen on hard times. Asked what was known of gentleman at large house & would I find work there? Learned nothing new. Then Coleridge hastened past.

Quickly ascended track to spy on house.

Many fruitless hours. At last Coleridge emerged, not in company of Wordsworth but with sister. Crept down hill to shadow them. Made way into wood & lingered amid autumn foliage. Observed them through bushes. Close as dared.

Discussion of much passion & urgency on both sides. Believed themselves alone. Coleridge first – much frustrated; present exercises going nowhere; hoped for greater collaboration.

Spirited rebuff from mistress. Work on brook had great potential. Wordsworth much inspired by work in hand.

Plot exactly as required: absence of established law & government; agents at liberty to act, etc. Poole in favour: thought it must benefit mankind more than anything yet done.

Coleridge's reply ardent, but lost in strong gust of wind.

Plot most devious & despicable.

No choice but to trust to post.

Memorandum from Joshua Baillie, Clerk at the Home Office, to John King, Thursday 12th October 1797

I have examined the register of passports issued to persons travelling to France.

I can confirm that a man named <u>William Wordsworth</u> has journeyed to that country on several occasions. The first time, he set out from Dover to be present in Calais on the anniversary of the storming of the Bastille. The second time, he departed these shores from Brighton on 28th November 1791. There is no record that he returned within the twelvemonth.

With regard to the other men, I can find no evidence that they have been in France.

Deposition of Joseph Johnson concerning William Wordsworth Esq.

I, Joseph Johnson, publisher, of St. Paul's Church-Yard, do hereby state all that I know of William Wordsworth Esq.

I first encountered this man nearly five years ago, when I published two poems of his upon his return from France. They were 'An Evening Walk. An Epistle, in Verse, Addressed to a Young Lady from the Lakes of the North of England' & 'Descriptive Sketches. In Verse.'

We corresponded on professional matters thereafter.

He asked me to publish certain satires in favour of constitutional reform, which he had produced with a clergyman named Wrangham. But I considered them to be of little interest. At the time, I believe he occupied lodgings in the same street as Mr Godwin, author of the 'Enquiry Concerning Political Justice'. He also attended assemblies at this man's house, as he said he once had meetings of the Revolution Society.

I do not know where he lives now, nor with what he is engaged. We have not exchanged letters in many months.

Extracts from the Notebooks of George Heaton

(Subsequently Deciphered)

Determined to penetrate Wordsworth's library & lay hands upon work so admired by Poole. Also to discover box or chest, most likely worn or battered, wherein observations of local country & accompanying maps & sketches.

Wordsworth & his mistress walk out most afternoons. Child roams free in all but most inclement weather. Servant not untypical in desiring nothing better than to doze in kitchen-parlour as soon as master has departed house.

Must bide time & await opportunity.

***

Great discoveries!

Wordsworth & mistress strode out in direction of Nether Stowey. Waited fifteen minutes, then approached house. Servant drowsing beside remains of lunch: dry bread, cheese & watered-down cider. Child nowhere to be seen.

Hastened to library. Walls lined with tomes; no small number of these French. Also lectures by Coleridge & book by Benjamin Constant:

Observations on the Strength of the Present Government in France & Upon the Necessity of Rallying Round It

No sign of box or chest, but pile of papers in loose order on desk. Work admired by Poole? Blank sheet on top. Directly beneath it list of names; some crossed through or amended.

Lennox

Wallace

Lacy

Nearby, on floor, book of ancient travels: author's name Samuel Purchas.

Fell open at pages with heavily marked passages. Used as key to secret cipher?

Surveyed room one more time. Eyes drawn to small cabinet formerly overlooked. Appeared to be store for quills & ink; also mundane financial accounts. Then, concealed at back, packet of letters tied with pink ribbon.

Composed in French. Date of composition not clear. Strange manner of writing. Water stained in places; from journey across English Channel? Signed _Annette_.

Means of communication with enemy? Conducted in cipher using aged travel book?

Considered removing & forwarding to London, but Wordsworth must suspect nothing. Readied to make copy. Then rasp of door & voices in hallway. Wordsworth back sooner than expected. Accompanied by Coleridge.

Hastily replaced letters & doubled over to window from whence effected exit. Crept into shadows. Remained long enough to be certain intrusion not detected.

Saw Coleridge depart house with books under arm. One of these by Purchas?

Letter to John King with No Signature, dated only "Thursday"

Sir

Further to yr inquiry of 9th inst. Racedown Lodge is a large farm-house surrounded by meadows and tracks <u>not</u> much used.

I believe Mr <u>Wordsworth</u> lived here 2 yrs with his Sister & a Childe & servant.

They lived very <u>private</u>.

They could see the <u>sea</u>. Also they could see it from a Hill near here called Golden Cap which was in times past a beacon for ships in the Channel.

I remain, etc

[*Margin entry in John King's hand:*
The house presently stands empty. No record can be discovered of any advertisement having been placed for a new tenant.]

Copy of Letter Sent by John King to Unknown Person in Edinburgh, Friday 13th October 1797

Sir

I must needs inquire whether anything be known of three men answering to the names of <u>Lennox</u>, <u>Wallace</u> and <u>Lacy</u>, whose whereabouts His Majesty's Government is most desirous to ascertain.

Little is known of these men beside their identities, which may be assumed for the purpose of carrying off some perfidious act of treason. It is thought they have established complicity with an individual or individuals in France, as well as with those who share their dubious allegiances within these shores. However, this will not be evident from a perusal of their writings, for they have at their disposal a cipher impenetrable to all but the most wary.

I urge you to be circumspect in your inquiries. It is to be presumed that they have access to a store of arms.

I remain, sir, etc

Extracts from the Notebooks of George Heaton
(Subsequently Deciphered)

Resolved to concentrate on C & his movements.

Observed him to set forth from cottage bearing knapsack. Air of excitement about his progress. Headed west to reach sea. Took out spyglass to scan horizon.

Secret assignation? By night with enemy landing party?

Sun low in sky. Coast of Wales visible across water. Large ship suddenly appeared on horizon. Sails furled & bare masts. Eerie look against red orb of setting sun.

C studied this intently. Took out pocket-book & made notes.

Ship vanished.

Continued on way. All time heading west. No recourse to maps or charts.

Arrived at place called Watchet. C to pass night at Bell Inn.

***

Continued west.

Route cleaved to coast.

C attentive to battlements of castle overlooking bay at Minehead.

Arrived at village called Porlock. Obtained provision & hastened on to ancient weir. Lingered some time. Struck off west again. This time uphill into dense foliage.

Almost stumbled upon him. Absorbed plundering crop of wild berries. Blue in colour. Known locally as *urts* or *worts*. Well past best, but told they help see in dark.

Explains appetite with which C set about them?

Continued west. Several sharp ascents. Forded stream cascading down to sea. Arrived at small church. Well-concealed from prying eyes. C paced back & forth. Paused to study inscription on gravestone. Awaiting someone? Sudden gasp of anguish. Features riven as if entrails sundered with red-hot metal. Stared about with expression of intense agony.

Ruse to see if he were followed?

C sank to ground & assaulted heavens. Rose again & staggered to corner of graveyard. Wrenched down pantaloons. Fulminous voiding of bowels. Respite sufficient to allow removal of small flask from knapsack.

Peregoric to check dysentery? Opiates & brandy?

Swallowed with shudder. Gathered energies & stumbled uphill bent double with cramps. Half mile up track came to smallholding called <u>Withycombe Farm</u>.

Supported himself against crumbling wall of wash-house.

Woman of house issued forth bearing pitchfork. Accompanied by pack of curs. Took him for vagrant or deserter from army?

Sudden cry of shock. Then addressed him by name.

C has walked this way before? On more than one occasion?

Begged her for shelter. She loathe to admit him; believed him purveyor of bloody flux? Thrust money into her hands & pleaded with her.

At last she gestured him toward barn.

Wail of baby from kitchen-parlour. Woman hastened inside; dogs with her.

Waited some minutes. No sign of woman. Anxious to keep distance from C?

Sneaked into barn.

C sweating profusely. Had flung off most clothes. Indignant at interruption. Incoherent protest. Thought me creditor? Clasped notebook jealously to chest. Incapable of robust defence. Collapsed onto straw barely conscious of surroundings.

Tore out scribbled pages. Went through discarded apparel. Nothing else of interest.

Departed barn & concealed myself at safe distance.

Several hours passed. C emerged. Fretful & agitated. Expression of man fallen short of great object. Did not continue west.

Myself in good spirits. More so than at any time since arriving in this region.

Memorandum from John King to the Duke of Portland, Tuesday 17th October 1797

I beg leave to acquaint Your Grace with the latest news from Nether Stowey, where Mr Heaton has excelled himself and – through a spirit of zealous inquiry born of his most fervent desire to earn the favour of a grateful nation – has obtained a copy of a secret and perplexing document borne west along the coast by Poole's secretary.

During this journey, which was undertaken alone, the man Coleridge paid particular attention to vessels in the Bristol Channel. He had recourse to a spyglass to study the coast and recorded his many observations in a pocket-book sealed with a clasp.

It is believed the object of this expedition must have been to keep an assignation with the enemy. If so, the intercepted document will prove anything but innocuous. However, as Your Grace may see, any person happening across it might conclude himself to be in possession of nothing more dangerous than a piece of nonsense rhyme.

By the features described, Mr Heaton conceives this rhyme to denote a special place west of Minehead; a location mooted for an ambush, or else the landing of an enemy skirmishing force. He has set himself the task of locating this.

However, it seems probable to me that the document employs a cipher altogether more labyrinthine in nature; one which is derived from an ancient and obscure travel book which Coleridge was seen to remove from the library at Alfoxton House the day before he commenced his journey.

I have therefore taken the liberty of submitting a copy of this document to our men who break code. I am hopeful we might thereby discover what designs these scoundrels purpose to carry out.

PS – Mr Heaton assures me the man Coleridge entertains no suspicion of this document having been seized, for he was unaware of his surroundings at the time, having had resort to opiates to check a dysentery. This indisposition so delayed his progress that, upon his recovery, he did not continue west, but at once returned to Nether Stowey exhibiting every sign of the greatest disappointment.

PPS – It is believed <u>ANNETTE</u> must be the alias of a person or persons responsible for overseeing a number of enemy spies presently at large within these shores. Several theories are considered, including that he is James Napper Tandy, the Irish outlaw, or even Thomas Paine himself. Both these men are known to have petitioned the Military Council in Paris with the aspiration of establishing themselves as Jacobin leaders within their respective countries.

Copy of Suspicious Document Found on the Person of Samuel Taylor Coleridge at Withycombe Farm, Friday 13th October 1797

In Xanadu did Kubla Khan
A stately pleasure-dome decree;
Where Alph, the sacred river, ran
Through caverns measureless to man
Down to a sunless sea.
So twice five miles of fertile ground
With walls and towers were compassed round:
And there were gardens bright with sinuous rills
Where blossomed many an incense-bearing tree,
And here were forests ancient as the hills
Enfolding sunny spots of greenery.
But O! that deep romantic chasm, which slanted
Down a green hill athwart a cedarn cover,
A savage place, as holy and enchanted
As e'er beneath a waning moon was haunted
By woman wailing for her demon lover:
From forth this chasm with hideous turmoil seething,
As if this earth in fast thick pants were breathing,
A might fountain momently was forced,
Amid whose swift half-intermitted burst
Huge fragments vaulted like rebounding hail,
Or chaffy grain beneath the thresher's flail:
And mid these dancing rocks at once & ever
It flung up momently the sacred river.
Five miles meandering with a mazy motion

Through wood and dale the sacred river ran,
Then reached the caverns measureless to man
And sank in tumult to a lifeless ocean;
And mid this tumult Kubla heard from far
Ancestral voices prophesying war.

Memorandum from the Duke of Portland to John King, Tuesday 17th October 1797

I have read your summation of the latest happenings at Nether Stowey.

You do right to be suspicious of this writing. I am no follower of the literary world, but I hold myself sufficiently acquainted with the laws of poetic diction to be certain that, as verse, it is not worthy of the effort of composition. The fact that this man Coleridge was chosen to bear it west along the coast, while all the time engaged in observations of the Bristol Channel, only serves to heighten my consternation.

You are to be in no doubt that deciphering this code is held a matter of the gravest importance at the highest level of Government. Were these men engaged in mere idle pursuits at such a time as this, they would be guilty of serving their country ill; but with each day that passes I grow more persuaded they ready an altogether darker form of treachery.

However, their immediate apprehension is not to be contemplated: close the net too soon & we will catch fewer fish. Rather, the local militia and yeomanry is to be placed in a state of readiness every bit as watchful as those forces which guard our southern and eastern shores.

PS – The reason I do not ask whether the woman is Wordsworth's mistress or his sister, is that I fear his depravity may not admit the distinction.

Deposition of Capt. John Roberts on the Military Career of Silas Tomkyn Comberbache, discharged insane from the 15th Light Dragoons, April 1794

I, Captain John Roberts of the 15th Light Dragoons, do hereby state all that I know of Silas Tomkyn Comberbache.

This man came to us from out of London, or so we thought. He seemed to be running from his debts, like many a volunteer. But I did hear he was a university man whose mind had become addled with philosophising. I also heard he had joined up under a false name after a spree of gambling & whoring.

He was with us near four months, which is sufficient time to obtain familiarity with military procedure and the drills & tactics of the local militia; and to know how to command men if called upon to do so. He was possessed of an uncanny ability to compel the attention of those around him when the mood took him. For a brief while, it was deemed this might be the making of him as a soldier.

However, Comberbache proved ill-suited to discipline. He was given to wild flights of fancy. He once contrived to shoot a bird from the sky and made such a pathetic show of pity at this, that it rendered him the laughing stock of his fellow recruits. He well nigh drove his commanding officer to distraction.

In the end, his defects won out & he was discharged insane after declaring Jacobin leanings under the influence of too much small beer.

I cannot say what became of him.

Letter to John King from Bristol, dated Wednesday 18th October 1797

Sir

You ought to be aware that, in the early part of 1795, an opprobrious young democrat – distinguishable at that time by his dishevelled locks & soiled stockings – took it upon himself to lecture an assembled throng in rooms above the Corn Market of this city. In his speech, he gave vent to the most dangerous principles and expressed all kind of Jacobin thought, claiming an undying bond with four *patriots*, all of whom had recently been found guilty of sedition and despatched to Botany Bay.

It soon became clear that this zealot must be quietened down for his own good. By a fortunate coincidence, an angry crowd mobbed his place of address that very night, subjecting him to threats and abuse. As a consequence, he chose to retire from public life about three months.

However, this retirement was nothing save a ruse. He emerged to proffer a course of lectures at the Assembly Coffee House on the Quay. In these, he lauded the revolutionary power of literature and spoke of Thomas Paine in the same breath as Mirabeau & Milton. He championed freedom of the press and compared the English Rebellion with recent events in France. He sought to propagate his opinions in a six-penny pamphlet.

We cannot know what desperate imaginings this recusant might have offered up next, for his lecturing career was abruptly ended by the passage of legislation later that year. But I can attest that, had he given those selfsame lectures the following twelvemonth, we would not any more be troubled by his presence.

The name of this man was *S. T. Coleridge*.

Letter to John King from Edinburgh, Undated

Sir

I write to report that a man answering to the name of Daniel <u>WALLACE</u> has taken up residence in an outlying district of this city.

He is a watch-maker from Fife & says he has come here to seek a position.

He is a papist & has been visited in his lodgings by a priest on more than one occasion.

He has attended secret meetings where a most violent lecture was spoken and copies of the *Rights of Man* were exchanged. A toast was proposed to its author & this <u>WALLACE</u> then rose to praise his namesake: a man who led a rebellion famed in these parts. Also at this meeting, the prophecy of Irish rebellion was met with cries of enthusiasm.

Another man present, Thomas <u>LENNOX</u>, is employed in the manufacture of oatmeal & is known to be a troublesome person.

Copy of letter despatched by John King to Edinburgh, Saturday 21st October 1797

Sir

You are to pursue your inquiries with the utmost vigour and urgency.

This man Wallace's conduct is cause for great alarm. As a person familiar with the manufacture of timepieces, he must be presumed to possess keen eyesight & a capability to master the intricate mechanics of modern weaponry.

You are also to pay close attention to the troublesome personage identified as Lennox & to maintain a constant look out for the third man, Lacy.

If it be necessary to conceive a pretext for searching these men's habitations, or to interrogate them, you are to do so without hesitation; being sure to employ only that degree of circumspection which is necessary to advance our cause rather than injure it.

I remain, sir, etc

PS – For the avoidance of doubt, the commonplace names of these men, whether assumed or otherwise, is no reason to presume them innocent. Were we to proceed on such a basis, it would imply that all those who mean to betray this nation will first single themselves out by the adoption of an outlandish alias.

Extract from the Journal of the Duke of Portland, Saturday 21st October 1797

I am just come from a soiree where all the talk is of Admiral Duncan's bold victory at Camperdown. To be sure, this fearless commander must be feted for generations to come. He did not hesitate to engage the Dutch fleet, although his numbers were inferior, and he soon brought to bear the skill and courage of our fighting men; the formidable power of our ships and guns. I am told the enemy fought with true valour, but half their ships are towed to shore in a state beyond repair.

News of this victory has met with scenes of great rejoicing in the streets of London. There is to be a service of thanksgiving at St Paul's Cathedral, where the Admiral himself shall carry the surrendered Dutch flag. Performances at the Theatre Royal will conclude with a representation of the Dutch fleet striking its colours to the tune of 'Rule Britannia'. And victory odes are to appear in the newspapers penned by the foremost poets of our time.

These tidings are, of course, most gratifying. But it would be folly to succumb to any feeling of complacency. The Dutch fleet is vanquished. Yet our gravest foe continues to muster troops and ships at the ports of Brest & Toulon; whether it be to attack Ireland, ally with the United Scotsmen, or to strike at our nearer shores direct.

Record of a Conversation between the Prime Minister & the Home Secretary, Tuesday 24th October 1797

The PRIME MINISTER commenced with certain sanguine remarks upon Admiral Duncan's splendid victory at Camperdown. He looked upon this to be incontrovertible evidence of the superior force of the British Navy, and confirmation that, as he had all along suspected, this was not diminished by the mutinies. The French must think twice before launching an invasion; particularly if it meant confronting a man so evidently their superior in valour and renown. A large gold medal must be struck in the Admiral's honour; and he should be raised to the peerage as Viscount Duncan of Camperdown with a pension of £3000 per annum.

The HOME SECRETARY concurred these tidings were most welcome. But he wished to observe that defeating the Dutch was one thing; resisting the French was entirely another. It was no secret that the latter continued to muster troops and ships at Brest and Toulon. And while Bonaparte might conclude the greater fortune lay elsewhere, he might with equal vindication determine a better opportunity to subdue Britain had never existed.

As to the conspiracies carried on within this country, these were entirely undiminished. He did not speak here of men who had overindulged in drink and boasted they would as soon shoot the King as a mad dog; or else set down a few lines of seditious doggerel. These were dangerous foes consumed by a spirit of inveterate animosity and depraved ambition. The victory at Camperdown might well elicit a desperate response from them.

The PRIME MINISTER replied that, if this were so, the Home Secretary should act to dismember their plots at once, making full use of the ministerial powers available to him.

The HOME SECRETARY said that, while it would be easy to make arrests now, this could only be done at the expense of discovering the true extent of such conspiracies. It was vital not to strike too soon; the more so, given the limited resources available to conduct such inquiries. On which note, he hoped they might resume discussion of a certain subject placed under review a fortnight previous.

The PRIME MINISTER said he was more than happy to oblige. He had now had chance to reflect at length upon the plan to evacuate the nation's gold bullion from the Bank of England to a secret location in the provinces. He was pleased to declare himself minded to grant it formal approval, with one or two minor revisions.

The HOME SECRETARY said he was delighted to learn this, but with respect the subject he wished to discuss was the budget available to his department; in particular as it regarded the premises from which he was being asked to oversee the security of the nation & the number of persons detailed to attend to this.

The PRIME MINISTER regretted any misunderstanding. He had not yet had chance to give this other subject the consideration it deserved. None the less, he hoped he might look forward to a successful and imminent resolution of the aforementioned inquiries, which could only help to precipitate a final determination of the matter.

Memorandum from John King to the Duke of Portland, Friday 3ʳᵈ November 1797

I must needs inform Your Grace of a most ill-informed and malicious pamphlet which has been found to be circulating in Portsmouth & Chatham, as well as among certain persons here in London.

As Your Grace will see, the author of this inflammatory publication conceives his specious argument by means of a direct attack upon the competence of the Home Office. He claims that the money would be better spent on the navy, not merely to ensure the security of the nation's coast, but to enhance prosperity through the protection of maritime trade.

It need hardly be stated that the content and timing of this publication are of especial concern for the grave threat posed to naval morale after that improvement occasioned by Admiral Duncan's victory. The nation can ill afford another mutiny, especially with Bonaparte encamped across the Channel and every report suggesting the means to transport his army to these shores is being rapidly assembled.

It is not known if this pamphlet has yet reached the eyes of the Prime Minister; but I would respectfully suggest it may be as well for Your Grace to ponder whether there are those in London whose interests are best served by such an eventuality.

Extract from 'Arguments in Favour of the Rapid Expansion of the Navy, Together with Certain Suggestions as to Where the Money May be Found to Accomplish This', first published October 1797

No matter how manifest the arguments in favour of expanding the navy, there are those who will say the monies do not exist to maintain such an indefatigable force. To refute their argument, however, it is only necessary to contrast the recent attainments of Admiral Duncan with those of other parties entrusted with the protection of the nation. It will soon be observed *that there is no requirement to raise taxes, merely to allocate funds differently*.

In particular, it is our lamentable duty to call into question the capability of the Home Office, which has in recent years presided over such a gratuitous expansion of those statutes deemed necessary to oversee the nation's domestic security. So much so, that leading members of the Opposition have become obliged to observe we exist under a reign of terror every bit as oppressive as that seen in the lands of our enemy.

Yet after the Traitorous Correspondence Act, the Treasonable Practices Act & the Seditious Meetings Act, what has this Ministry actually achieved to vindicate the passage of such measures?

Not so long ago, we were told that two men would suffer the harshest penalty for aiding and abetting the landing of Colonel Tate's *Legion Noir*. But it turned out that the evidence against them relied solely upon the dubious testimony of French prisoners of war: evidence which, to no one's surprise but that of His Grace the Duke of Portland, fell apart under the most elementary cross-examination.

And what of the operation of a domestic "secret service"? (Although we hesitate to use that term for a bloated network of spies and informers whose currency is tittle-tattle, hearsay & gossip which did nothing to warn of Colonel Tate's impending arrival upon these shores.)

We do not dispute there are conspirators at large; nor that such persons are guilty of the most heinous treason in conniving at the encouragement of a French invasion. Yet we are inclined to wonder if the extent of these conspiracies is exaggerated to justify the vast expense incurred in opposing them. It is our understanding that a number of Government departments are permitted to draw on secret service funds to whatever extent necessary without scrutiny from the Treasury. This is tantamount to shovelling the nation's wealth down a vast and bottomless Pitt.

In short, it is our contention that the great majority of monies allocated for the purpose of domestic security would be better spent upon enlarging that grand bulwark of the nation, the navy, to a size that is the true envy of the world. This would represent a far more advantageous use of funds than the maintenance of an expensive, ineffective and malignant security operation, whose existence is an affront to the very cause of Liberty the people of this country are so proud to uphold.

Extract from the Journal of the Third Duke of Portland, Saturday 4th November 1797

Truly this pamphlet is an outrage: almost certainly a French plot to sow the seeds of discontent at the highest level of government & if so a ------ good one.

But what if it is not? What if it be the work of one envious of the powers I am granted & ambitious to usurp them by painting my Office in the blackest light?

I must evince a haughty disdain for these calumnies, safe in the knowledge that to accuse me of doing nothing is to accuse the hawk of idling at the very moment it hovers above its prey & deliberates when to commence the deadly plunge.

Memorandum from the Duke of Portland to John King, Monday 6th November 1797

I have perused the pamphlet you sent me and hold it such a piece of arrant mischief, entertaining so little understanding of the true responsibilities of government, that I must consider its author less a friend to our seamen than to Bonaparte himself.

It is especially vexatious to read such tomfoolery when we stand upon the verge of penetrating the conspiracy at Nether Stowey. Yet to arrest these villains out of irritation at the crapulous outpourings of one who would place the entire defence of this nation at the mercy of an Atlantic tempest must be the height of folly; especially when we possess the chance to break their cipher & thereby learn much of other traitors at large in this nation.

I must again urge that every priority be given to establishing the full import of the document borne west from Nether Stowey; even if this necessitates many days of work.

I would also have you instruct Heaton to lay aside his own theories – for which we do not pay him – and confine his presence to the vicinity of Alfoxton, where he should make ready to pursue these men when they attempt another excursion west; as I believe they surely shall.

Extracts from the Notebooks of George Heaton
(Subsequently Deciphered)

Scenery described bears great resemblance to that passed on way to church. Features & measurements most precise, as if anxious to get them right?

Riddle where X (X̲anadu) marks the spot? What for? Ambuscade?

***

W & C have subsided into listlessness. TP entirely occupied with tannery. No excursions by day or night. No letters received of any interest.

Response to news of Camperdown? Or to failure of C's expedition?

***

Enlisted aid of old man to survey coast west of Minehead.

Aged & malodorous sea-dog. Did little at first to merit gratuity. Swore blind he knew of no cavern large enough to store provisions. Bored me with tiresome folklore.

After preposterous yarn about vengeful sea-bird, seized with irritation & demanded to know of him whether he conned any place round here beginning with X.

"Why, ziree!" he exclaimed, "only the moor itself."

***

What if C meant to demarcate place beginning with EX?

Have examined chart & discovered place named *Hurlstone* Point few miles west of Minehead. Denoted by fragments of vaulting rock – e.g. hurled stone – in C's riddle?

Five miles inland from this place – exactly same distance as from Xanadu to sea in riddle – lies isolated village on moor.

Name? EXFORD

Letter to John King from Edinburgh, Undated

Sir

I have inspected the room of Daniel <u>WALLACE</u>.

Its walls are rude & bare save for a ragged cloth. There is a space beneath the floorboards, but I could find nothing concealed. There is a small table & chest which was locked. The chest does not weigh much.

I also found some books hidden beneath a straw mattress:
- 1 copy of *Rights of Man* & another by T Paine: *Common Sense*
- 1 pamphlet in support of the French government
- 1 work of Scotch history & 2 more of foreign travel

I could see no letters from France. The only other sheet of paper contained a few lines of verse which the landlord, one Mr Buchanan, says <u>WALLACE</u> has scribbled in the hope of making an epic on Scotch history in the manner of *Mr Milton*.

I am not so certain about this. I have only heard <u>WALLACE</u> to say that if nothing turns up, he means to go to sea as there is lucrative reward in the trade with Iceland.

PS – Mr Buchanan recalls no visitor by the name of <u>LACY</u>. The only visitor in recent days has been a priest, who bore a packet of watches which I am told <u>WALLACE</u> mends in return for victual. I did not see this packet.

Record of a Conversation between the Prime Minister & the Home Secretary, Tuesday 14th November 1797

The HOME SECRETARY explained his final revisions to the plan to evacuate the nation's gold bullion from the Bank of England to a secret location in the provinces.

The PRIME MINISTER declared himself satisfied with these and announced the choice arrived at to be most felicitous. He then inquired whether the Home Secretary knew anything of a pamphlet rumoured to be gaining admiration in places such as Chatham and Portsmouth

The HOME SECRETARY said he did and that his cognisance of it was sure proof of the fallacious rhetoric of this publication. He considered it to be nothing but inflammatory rabble rousing, which deserved to meet with haughty disdain from any person in possession of a true appreciation of the manifold responsibilities of government.

The PRIME MINISTER said he must none the less feel some unease at its effect upon naval morale. Furthermore, it was his information that their powers of disdain would be tested to the full by the imminent publication of a scurrilous print, which would depict the Duke of Portland shovelling the nation's wealth into a bottomless Pitt: a representation they might be sure flattered neither of them.

The HOME SECRETARY replied that matters of government policy, especially when these concerned the defence of the realm, could never be dictated by the whim of opprobrious picture sketchers. He hoped this did not signify a resumption of those rumours which had begun to circulate in the summer suggesting he might be replaced by a person of greater vigour; or that responsibility for domestic order would soon be arrogated within the office of Prime Minister.

The PRIME MINISTER declared these rumours to be a manifest scandal; patently the work of persons sympathetic to the French cause, who schemed to promote discord at the heart of government by exploiting the fact his ministry was a coalition of men who had formerly opposed one another.

The HOME SECRETARY agreed that divide and rule appeared to be the guiding motive of this pamphlet.

The PRIME MINISTER said he hoped the Home Secretary would concur with him in advocating a most vehement response to confound its central argument.

The HOME SECRETARY replied it had always been his principle to recollect the maxim: close the net too soon and one will catch fewer fish.

The PRIME MINISTER did not dispute this, but observed that, in the aftermath of Camperdown, the climate of public opinion was somewhat altered. It might be advisable to ensure those conspiracies the Home Office tracked did not come to nothing; and that the authors of such plots did not melt away like so many phantoms.

The HOME SECRETARY said he could not help but recall his office had on several occasions been prevented from exhibiting its great contribution to the security of the nation by a risk of compromising informers or else the high cost of prosecutions. It was clear it required more funding, not less, and this must be addressed before a time came when, through want of men, information vital to the country's defence was overlooked with perilous consequences. In the meanwhile, he could do no more than ensure every circumstance was taken into account when it was determined what proceedings to instigate against those whose treacherous behaviour placed the nation in such grave jeopardy.

The PRIME MINISTER observed that nothing else could be expected of any person in possession of a true appreciation of the manifold responsibilities of government.

Memorandum from the Duke of Portland to John King, Tuesday 14th November 1797

I wish to express my dismay that we have yet to obtain any purposeful interpretation of the document carried west by Poole's amanuensis from Nether Stowey.

I am cognisant of the fact that there exists a considerable burden of work upon those we employ to decrypt coded correspondence. But I fear this delay is as much the outcome of a general complacency in the aftermath of Admiral Duncan's victory. I would therefore have you remind everyone in this Office that the French do not cease to mass their forces at major ports; and that Bonaparte actively canvasses opinion on the best means to subdue this island once and for all.

I expect to receive very shortly, if not a comprehensive decryption of these writings, then a considered opinion of the nature and complexity of the cipher employed, together with a detailed estimate of the time required to break it.

PS – I also await substantive developments in your quest for the men whose names were discovered on the list in the library at Alfoxton House.

Copy of letter despatched by John King to Edinburgh, Wednesday 15th November 1797

Sir

I must express my dissatisfaction at what has been despatched concerning the man Wallace. The investigation of his quarters I deem to be anything but complete. Insufficient attention has been paid to the locked chest, the contents of which must be considered of greater import than its weight.

I also demand, as a matter of priority, a full inventory of every book in his possession, as well as a precise transcription of his lines of patriotic doggerel. With regard to each book, you are to indicate whether there is any sign of frequent recourse to certain passages; for example, the existence of heavily marked or annotated pages.

I also desire to know the name of the priest who visits Wallace in his room, which is to be submitted with a full description of his person.

I remain, sir, etc

PS – Arrangements can be made to have Wallace examined by an officer of the law on a separate matter if this is deemed necessary to obtain access to the locked chest.

Extracts from the Notebooks of George Heaton
(Subsequently Deciphered)

Am told they do not pay me to break codes, but to be shadow.

Cannot expect to see Xford, unless in pursuit of C.

Commanded to penetrate W's library & copy secret letters from France. Also to obtain entire list of Scottish names. Is one Buchanan? Is one priest?

***

Little to note.

W suffers effects of chill & keeps to house. C taken up with garden & pig; few assignations with TP.

Ability to operate in covert manner reduced as leaves descend from trees.

***

C, W & sister departed Alfoxton this pm.

Proceeded along coast with full knapsack. Frequent recourse to spyglass. Broke journey at Watchet, as C did last time.

***

Change of direction. Did not continue west, but made inland as if to skirt moor.

Pursued them at some distance, adopting varied gait.

C rehearsed speeches in most isolated places. Wild gesticulations directed at no one in particular. Not near enough to overhear words. No chance to intercept message, if this committed to paper.

Reached place called Dulverton.

Clear from local charts they make for X̲ by circuitous route.

Consumed with sense of great anticipation.

***

Sudden fork to reach coast at Lynton by way of Withypool & Simonsbath.

Why shy away from X̲? Did they deduce themselves followed & choose to abort plan?

***

Arranged with man at inn where they lodge. Favourably disposed, so long as well rewarded. Told me they partook of hearty supper. Their conversation at first dreary; homily to appeal of moor. Could not be more specific.

Tongues loosed after further bottle. Man with scar on cheek (W) railed against established custom & urged representation of ordinary men.

Difficult to discern all of what was said. Spoke in hushed tones.

Mention of dark crime & ship carrying deadly crew?

Proposed trip to continent by way of Hamburg?

Memorandum purported to be the work of "Maddison", the Government Code-Breaker, Not Dated

It is the most desirable quality of any cipher, and the greatest testimony to its creator, that it should persuade the enemy it would be fanciful to regard it as such.

In this instance, we are confronted with a poetic composition which would certainly be dismissed as nonsense rhyme, were it not for the fact that it describes a coastal topography known to be of interest to the enemy and concludes with a prophecy of war irrespective of what has gone before.

Much work remains to be done to decipher this code in its entirety. The following comments are submitted by way of a preliminary illustration of how it may be conceived to operate.

THEORY 'A'

The recipient of this verse would identify the precise location described from one of a number of choices formerly discussed & derive an indication of our preparedness for military action at that place by the final word of the message, which would be either "war" or "peace".

If this were the case, we should expect to intercept further verses passed to French agents, each concluding with the word "war" or "peace".

THEORY 'B'

It seems more probable to me that the aged book of exotic travels penned by Samuel Purchas – from which the subject is taken & which the messenger was seen to have in his possession – constitutes the key to this cipher.

[*Margin entry in John King's hand:* Important.]

The relevant passage from this book is:

"In Xanadu did Cublai Can build a stately palace, encompassing sixteene miles of plaine ground with a wall, wherein are fertile meadows, pleasant springs, delightful streams, & all sorts of beasts of chase and game, and in the midst thereof a sumptuous house of pleasure, which may be removed from place to place."

I would note that the following curious alterations have been made:

- In the message, but not the book, the river is given a special name: <u>ALPH</u>.
- In the book, Purchas says the palace encompasses sixteen miles of ground. But in the message this is given a different measurement: "twice five" or <u>TEN</u>.

I cannot but observe that these changes serve to convey the first and last syllables of the property under suspicion, <u>Alfoxton</u>.

I would note also that the name Khan and the subject of water, when the latter is rendered into

[Page or pages missing]

Memorandum from John King to the Duke of Portland, Tuesday 21st November 1797

I cannot but share Your Grace's alarm that a devious and despicable attempt has been made to conceal the name of Alfoxton in the document borne west by the traitor, Coleridge. It is not to be conceived that a man who has made detailed observations of a place coveted by the enemy, and who has formerly pronounced a series of incendiary lectures upon *the revolutionary power of literature*, should while away his time on a pedestrian tour in the composition of meaningless rhyme.

To this must be added the latest tidings from Nether Stowey, which I cannot read without consternation that Heaton's identity has been penetrated, notwithstanding his admirable powers of disguise. For it appears that these men now mean to abandon their conspiracy and smuggle themselves to Hamburg – which is a well-known place of traffic between the United Irishmen & their supporters abroad – there to await a more favourable opportunity for the perpetration of treachery.

Memorandum from John King to the Duke of Portland, Tuesday 21st November 1797

I write with great haste to inform Your Grace that I have received tidings of a most grievous nature from Edinburgh, where the man Wallace is reported to have fled the city.

Urgent inquiries are instituted to establish his whereabouts. But the chances of doing so appear small, for he has not been seen since the 16th inst. (Several days were permitted to elapse before the decision was taken to inform me of his disappearance.)

Upon receipt of this news, I despatched orders for the other suspect, Thomas Lennox, to be confined. I also gave out that every measure is to be contemplated to discover the priest, who is suspected of having furnished Wallace with a packet of books under the pretence these were timepieces.

I regret to inform Your Grace that no occasion had been found to examine these books – one of which may have been the work by Purchas – nor to ascertain the contents of a locked chest kept in Wallace's lodgings. It must also be presumed that no sight had been obtained of the verse he was composing, in order to establish whether this described a particular place or concluded with the word "war".

NB – Your Grace will not need to be told Scotland is a wild and desolate place where a man opposed to the Government might obtain secure habitation among those on whom he can depend to conceal his presence.

Memorandum from the Duke of Portland to John King, Tuesday 21st November 1797

I hereby command you to draw up orders for the immediate apprehension of Thomas Poole and his secretary, as well as of Wordsworth and the woman with him. The Poor Man's Club in Nether Stowey is to be disbanded and generous reward offered for the recovery of any weapon stored secretly.

PS – Heaton should be recalled to service in London at once, where it is imperative that we discover more of what is contemplated in certain taverns of this city.

Excerpts from 'Jottings of a Militiaman in the Time of Bonaparte', by Augustus Falconer, first published by his grandson (1884)

Late one afternoon toward the end of November, our commander was summoned to attend the local magistrate, Sir P Hale Bar[t] of Boymore near Bridgewater, on a matter of great urgency. His assistance was required in the apprehension of a set of dangerous Jacobins, who had already made observations of the Severn Sea and were now conniving at the sack of Bristol.

So it was that I came to be part of a small detachment, or skirmishing force, despatched to Alfoxton House at first light the following morning by obscure tracks, in order not to excite attention in Nether Stowey where the main body of men would be deployed. We were accompanied by an officer of the law and his sour-faced assistant, who professed to know the property exceeding well and how it might be penetrated, whether by stealth or direct assault. Our party was augmented by members of the Volunteer Corps, among them a gamekeeper and several others skilful in the use of fowling pieces.

I recollect a feeling of intense excitement as we made our way across the moor. Not a single man shivered, although the cold was most extreme. We left a sharpshooter stationed among the trees overlooking the house and plunged downhill, pursuing a broad track slippery with frost. On several occasions, I thought I perceived a movement at an upstairs casement.

At the corner of the drive, we passed a small building from which, amid the barking of curs, an old man issued forth. He had a niggardly, squinting expression which soon turned to alarm at witnessing our preparedness for combat. He stuttered out an inquiry as to how long before the French were here. The officer bade him hold his tongue and said this was a matter of domestic security, at which he seemed placated.

We proceeded up the drive, all the time expecting an ambuscade from among the trees, but we heard nothing except the trickle of running water. Our route prescribed a great loop and then, all of a sudden, the house appeared in view. We advanced across open ground to either side of the officer and his assistant, but met with no resistance. However, it was too early to presume that we had the advantage of surprise.

The officer gave a harsh rap at the door, which seemed to echo back off the hillside, and demanded the inhabitants open up in the name of His Majesty. There was no sound from within and no movement at any window. The officer did not pause, but gave a second rap, gesturing at us to prepare to storm the building.

Suddenly the door opened and a servant-woman rushed forth to implore mercy. She was at once arraigned by two soldiers. The rest of us surged into the house, hastening from room to room, all the time wary of attack at close quarters. One trooper plunged his bayonet into heavy curtains, such was the expectation the rebels must be concealed about the place. We pressed upstairs and, in one room, only the high-pitched whimpering of a young boy wrapped in bedclothes saved him from destruction.

A few minutes more, and it was clear that we had located the only two persons residing in the house. The assistant busied himself examining a desk in the library. Several volunteers were detailed to search the property from top to bottom for a store of weapons. The rest of us were summoned outside to await further orders. By this means, we served as witness to the officer's interrogation of the servant-woman.

- You are certain they are gone to London?

She nodded, but kept her eyes on the ground.

- And they went alone?

She assented again.

- On what business?

She shook her head.

- Things will go much better for you, if you tell me all that you know. Do they seek to secure a passage to the continent there, or do they make for the eastern coast?

She shook her head again.

- If you know what is good for you, you will tell me.

The woman raised her head, but upon encountering his scrutiny she gave way to the full compass of her distress and could not be prevailed upon to reveal anything more.

She was escorted away, as was the small boy whose interests were best served by a perpetual severance from the guardianship of these people.

***

We were ordered to proceed with all haste to Nether Stowey, for it was concluded that the absence of resistance at this house must presage a greater requirement for troops there. At the same time, a messenger was despatched to urge a pursuit of the tenant of Alfoxton who, whether by cunning or good fortune, had evaded the trap set for him and was now proceeding to the capital, with what malign purpose nobody yet knew.

Some attributed his escape to the machinations of an enemy double-agent. Others declared it an arrant piece of conjuring and told how more than one villager had witnessed this man muttering dark incantations as he tramped the local byways.

A fast march we had of it along the highway, but, as we approached Nether Stowey, I could discern no sounds of combat. We left the road and approached the garden of a small cottage across glebe land where a number of soldiers moved to and fro.

One of these leapt over the carcass of a butchered pig and announced that both rebels had been seized without so much as a shot fired. A group of local labourers had assembled, but they did not carry arms, only tools of their trade which might double as such. All resistance had disappeared when several of them were arrested on suspicion of having sworn a secret oath.

I later heard that the secretary was wrestled to the ground as he made for his master's house to raise the alarm. He was pinioned down among the fallen leaves of a lime tree and confined in chains, all the time raging against his treatment which he declared to shame his country. Meanwhile his wife, greatly mistaken as to the cause of his apprehension, harangued her prone husband for living beyond his means and screamed to all and sundry that Mr Poole would pay whatever was owed.

Eventually the prisoner was led away to a volley of abuse from a band of hastily assembled patriots; soon to be followed by his master, who contrived to maintain an appearance of bemused gentility throughout. He called to one acquaintance to send to Over Stowey and tell them he was not harmed, but rather anticipated his early release as soon as his captors realised their mistake.

I was detailed to aid the search of both men's premises; a task which continued long after the secretary's wife had enacted preparations to decamp to Bristol. The pits at the tan-yard stank to High Heaven, but every man remained constant in his allotted task.

It may not be remembered now, but the militia earned much renown for its action that day. Many a man slept easier knowing that the defence of the local shores was the preserve of so capable a force. Certainly this was the view of the magistrate, who issued orders that each man should enjoy an extra ration of fresh meat.

Letter from Richard Bickerstaff to his Uncle in Herefordshire, the first part of which is dated 23rd November 1797

Sir

I have met no one in Bath who looks with favour upon our commercial proposition, save for a gouty gentleman in Paragon Buildings, who, if truth be told, seems more desirous of entering into negotiations concerning certain female relatives of his.

Fortunately I have obtained the names of several merchants in the City of London. I now mean to direct our quest for capital to that place. As to the high rate of return they shall require, I will consider our bargaining position & set out my thoughts below prior to posting.

***

I beg you to allow me the indulgence of a digression while we halt to change horses, for I believe you would find tolerable diversion in several of my fellow travellers; among them a dyspeptic clergyman & a stout lady of the dowager persuasion, neither of whom the spa-water has cured of their ills.

Yet I chiefly find myself enthralled by another couple; a man and woman who hold themselves aloof and travel in respectable garb, although not, I believe, with likewise intention. There is no small degree of intimacy between them & they whisper together often. Yet the man is somewhat older and there is no sign they are connubially joined. I have passed more than a few miles figuring to myself a scenario: an elopement, perhaps, or even that he has plucked her from a *bagnio*!

***

We are all of us muffled against the cold, but the man has been particularly reluctant to display his features. Now I know why, for as we stepped down from the coach, I happened to observe some kind of mark or scar upon his cheek!

I believe they mean to keep some kind of assignation. For, when we narrowly avoided mishap due to ice and the clergyman vociferated his opinion we would end the day in a snow-drift, the man started and became morose & preoccupied.

My supposition is this: the woman is some nymph he has seduced into thinking he can elevate before the London throng. They travel in disguise because she is not without protectors. (Judging by the scar on his cheek, there have been other occasions when exception was taken to his conduct!)

What do you think, sir? Do you agree there can be no smoke without fire? Or do you splutter into your breakfast viands & swear this nephew of yours reads too much Mrs Radcliffe?

***

Forget Mrs R! No pen could trump the astounding *denouement* to our journey which has indeed taken place!

We had got within a few miles of London when I heard a distant drumming of hooves, which rapidly transformed itself into a precipitous thunder. Surmising this to be the pursuit of which the man must be afraid, I surveyed his features; but he betrayed no emotion.

Instead it was my fellow passengers who exhibited trepidation. The dowager commenced furtive operations to conceal certain items about her person. The next sounds can only have confirmed her fears. There was the discharge of a gun and a sharp exchange of voices. Our coach juddered to a halt, the door was wrenched open, and an imperious voice bade us descend in the name of His Majesty.

I was ejected from the carriage by a violent shove, which I must attribute to the clergyman. When I regained my balance, I was confronted with the sight of three or four soldiers circling on horseback & a number of their compatriots already dismounted with weapons arrayed! All were scarlet with exertion and their apparel was bespattered with dirt. As soon as we stood before them – all save the dowager who had fainted quite away – one of the horsemen addressed us: "We seek one named Wordsworth."

I glanced toward the man with the scarred face and saw him exchange a fearful look with his female companion.

But he stepped forward and identified himself as the passenger they sought. His pursuers did not stand on ceremony, but at once jostled about him, wrestling him to the ground and stripping his outer garments in search of concealed weapons. Then he was clamped in irons!

At this, the woman rushed forward to intervene, but she was repelled with no small force. Then she, too, was arraigned by her captors who obtained much amusement in addressing her as *Mistress Wordsworth* and such like.

Each passenger was searched in turn, despite vehement protest at this violation of our liberties. It was some minutes before we were permitted to regain the coach. Upon our arrival in London, we were required to submit sworn testimony as to what we had observed during the journey; and to place on record our name and place of abode.

I must confess that I felt no small irritation at my own treatment & a resultant sympathy with the woman in her plight. But when I reflect that we may have carried in our midst a deserter, or even a French spy, I find this sentiment to be greatly reduced!

I remain, Sir, your humble & obedient nephew,

Richard Bickerstaff

Memorandum from John King to the Duke of Portland, Saturday 25th November 1797

I rejoice to inform Your Grace that the conspiracy at Nether Stowey is broken up and its progenitors deprived of liberty. Poole and his secretary were seized at their homes. They are to be transported to London in chains to undergo proper examination, this being no matter for the assizes. The army of poor men is entirely disbanded.

Wordsworth and his companion had already departed for London. They were intercepted only after a most admirable pursuit by officers. It is not known what prompted their sudden flight.

The tenant of Alfoxton is presently confined under guard at Crown Street prior to his appearance before the Privy Council. He shall then be transported to a cell at Coldbath Fields, where he is to be held in readiness for trial. His companion was also taken into custody, but no sense can be obtained from her. It is doubtful any advantage will accrue from subjecting her to the same proceedings.

There is much reason to think the coming days shall see an irresistible strengthening of the case against these men. I anticipate that, when they become cognisant of the true gravity of their situation, it will not be long before one of them treats to turn King's Evidence against the others.

Record of a Conversation between the Prime Minister & the Home Secretary, Monday 27th November 1797

The PRIME MINISTER conveyed his satisfaction at this news of the apprehension of a gang of Jacobins who had conspired with the French to go one better than Colonel Tate's *Legion Noir* and destroy Bristol. He trusted it would not be long until they appeared before the Board of Interrogation of the Privy Council.

The HOME SECRETARY affirmed it would not. Furthermore, it was his strong conviction that these arrests must force the French to think twice about the dependability of their allies within these shores; a matter of no small importance given the undoubted existence of other such conspiracies. Conspiracies, he might add, which would never be combated by a strategy dependent solely upon expansion of the navy. Should the Prime Minister require further proof of this, he need only ask himself why the suspect Wordsworth had been captured just a few miles from London.

The PRIME MINISTER invited the Home Secretary to elaborate.

The HOME SECRETARY said there were strong grounds to believe this man had been on his way to the capital to commit some desperate act. It was not impossible this would have entailed the assassination of a prominent political figure.

The PRIME MINISTER desired to know what precautions were taken to ensure the prisoner could pose no threat as he was transported from the Tower to answer the inquiries of the Privy Council.

The HOME SECRETARY stated that, since the prisoner was in fact confined close by in Crown Street, he would have no opportunity to escape during his brief conveyance to the place of interrogation. He would then be transported to Coldbath Fields, which was a most efficacious facility for the confinement of dangerous men, not known for nothing in certain circles as the English Bastille.

The PRIME MINISTER wondered whether these measures went far enough, or whether it might be desirable for Wordsworth to be confined in Coldbath Fields at once, notwithstanding its greater distance from Whitehall. Indeed he did not see why this man was not imprisoned in the Tower.

The HOME SECRETARY said he looked forward to a time when all such questions concerning the premises available to the Home Office might be resolved; not least the continued existence of the Alien Office, which it was his understanding a new Act of Parliament must soon clarify.

The PRIME MINISTER replied that he did not foresee any circumstances in which this legislation would not be enacted. But its passage might take several months, by which time he trusted these conspirators would be brought to justice: an outcome needful to ensure the continued vigilance of the public, and to publish abroad the Government's determination to crush all those whose avowed ambition appeared to be nothing less than the destruction of the greatest nation on earth.

Part Two

The Guardian Crook of Law

"I hope you will be cautious in writing or expressing your political opinions ... the Ministers have great powers."

Richard Wordsworth,
Letter to his younger brother William, 1794

Transcript of the appearance of William Wordsworth before the Board of Interrogation of the Privy Council, 29th November 1797

Among those in attendance:

The Prime Minister
His Grace the Duke of Portland, Home Secretary
The Lord Chancellor, Lord Loughborough
Sir John Scott, Attorney General
Sir John Mitford, Solicitor General
The Prisoner

***

Attorney General: Do you confirm that you are William Wordsworth, lately tenant of Alfoxton House in the county of Somerset; and, prior to that, occupant of Racedown Lodge in the county of Dorset?

Solicitor General: Let it be noted the prisoner inclined his head by way of affirmation.

Home Secretary: I trust there is to be no attempt to obstruct the proceedings of this inquiry.

Attorney General: Mr Wordsworth, you should not consider yourself bound to answer our questions here today. But you would do well to reflect upon the consequences of your not doing so.

Prisoner: Then might I venture to speak?

Lord Chancellor: That is in accordance with our wishes, sir.

Prisoner: In which case, I demand to know what is the purpose of this inquisition. By what right am I held? Of what am I accused?

Solicitor General: You are confined pending the definitive establishment of certain facts. As to the nature of any accusation, that is yet to be determined.

Attorney General: It is not the purpose of this inquiry to extract a confession, but to oversee the commission of justice. If you have nothing to conceal, it is in your interest to answer the questions put to you faithfully, without subterfuge or digression.

Lord Chancellor: Well, what do you say?

Solicitor General: Let it be noted the prisoner inclined his head by way of affirmation.

Home Secretary: Let us waste no further time, but proceed with the examination. What motive brought you to Alfoxton House this past summer?

Prisoner: A desire for improved society.

Lord Chancellor: I beg your pardon?

Prisoner: My sister and I were too much isolated in Dorset. Our friends at Nether Stowey recognised this and made inquiries regarding the lease of Alfoxton. We were pleased to find it suited our needs entirely.

Attorney General: When you make reference to your friends at Nether Stowey, I take it you mean Thomas Poole and his secretary?

Prisoner: I would hardly term Coleridge his secretary – far from it – but, yes, I do.

Attorney General: Is it not true that Poole supports Coleridge, his wife and a child?

Prisoner: I believe so, but I would not posit Coleridge to be anything other than independent.

Attorney General. Indeed.

Home Secretary: None the less, to return to the question of your decision to rent Alfoxton, it would seem strange, would it not, in view of your desire to obtain more frequent intercourse with your friends, that you lighted upon a dwelling so entirely suited to the continuance of an existence characterised by seclusion and secrecy?

Prisoner: It does not seem strange to me.

Home Secretary: Why ever not?

Prisoner: As a philosopher and poet, it is my preference to seek out places of solitude and tranquillity; that I might engage in contemplation without disturbance.

Attorney General: But does not Coleridge also style himself a philosopher and poet? Yet he inhabits a small cottage in Nether Stowey.

Prisoner: There are considerable differences between us, as men.

Home Secretary: They are not inconvenient differences if they allow you to indulge a marked propensity for occupying large, secluded dwellings blessed with excellent prospects of the sea.

Prisoner: I do not think my taste in property a crime; certainly not one worthy of the consideration of the Privy Council.

Prime Minister: None the less, in times such as these, with the nation under constant threat of invasion, one might wonder whether a true patriot would consider it his duty to do something more than sit philosophising?

Solicitor General: Let it be noted the prisoner inclined his head.

Attorney General: We shall no doubt return to the nature of your philosophical activities, Mr Wordsworth. But certain information has been obtained which suggests that you have not always coveted a life of sedentary musing. Is that so?

Prisoner: I have no reason to doubt the veracity of your information; only that it could be of any interest to so august a body of men.

Lord Chancellor: Allow us to be the judges of that.

Attorney General: Very well, then. Please to contradict any of the following. Upon leaving university six years ago, you lingered in London some months with no evident purpose. During this time, your associations led you to attend a number of radical sermons, as well as meetings of the Revolution Society.

Prisoner: I do not recall any such sermons.

Home Secretary: But you do not deny the meetings?

Prisoner: We speak of a brief interlude six years ago. I cannot be expected to remember every moment of my past life; nor indeed am I the same man as I was then.

Attorney General: Perhaps your memory of your residence in London three years ago is clearer. You do not deny, I suppose, that you took lodgings in Charlton Street, a few doors down from William Godwin, author of the 'Enquiry Concerning Political Justice'? Nor that you attended numerous gatherings at his house while they were still lawful? Nor that you indulged yourself – with one Francis Wrangham – in the production of satires lampooning the monarchy and parliament?

Prisoner: I take it you refer to Mr Godwin, author of 'Caleb Williams; or Things As They Are', a novel concerning the persecution of an unfortunate secretary by those more powerful than himself?

Lord Chancellor: Take heed, sir.

Home Secretary: We do not concern ourselves with works of imagination here, Mr Wordsworth.

Attorney General: I observe you do not contradict any of the above. Nor, I suppose, do you deny that you have had two poems printed by a man with levelling tendencies, Joseph Johnson of St Paul's: he who first published the 'Rights of Man'.

Prisoner: I do not deny that.

Attorney General: Then perhaps you would care to tell us whether you submitted any other work for his consideration?

Prisoner: I do not recollect so.

Home Secretary: Oh come. You do not recall a manuscript in which you signed yourself 'A Republican' and defended the execution of His Majesty the King of France? This was found among your papers in the library at Alfoxton House.

Prisoner: I do not remember seeking to publish such a piece, which I believe was your question.

Home Secretary: Your answers are not all they could be to assure us of your loyalty as a subject; nor of your innocuous disposition as a bucolic philosopher.

Attorney General: But that is far from all, is it?

Prisoner: I do not follow you.

Lord Chancellor: He means to ask whether you were ever in France?

Prisoner: It is a country I visited before the present war, yes.

Attorney General: And one in whose language you are tolerably proficient?

Prisoner: Indeed.

Home Secretary: Then perhaps you would care to enlighten

us as to the nature of your philosophical discoveries in that place?

Prisoner: In truth, my time there was uneventful. On the first occasion, I arrived with a friend on the anniversary of the fall of the Bastille. We proceeded south and walked many miles through the Alps.

Lord Chancellor: You are not unaccustomed to long marches?

Prisoner: I was a young man at the time.

Attorney General: And your next sojourn?

Prisoner: I passed some months in Orleans, where I was fortunate to have the benefit of several introductions.

Home Secretary: Introductions? Introductions to what? The local Jacobin club?

Prisoner: That is not what I meant.

Attorney General: Did you attend meetings of the local Jacobin club?

Prisoner: I do not remember. It is possible I attended one or two, out of politeness to a friend.

Prime Minister: It seems to me you ought to be more careful in your choice of friends.

Attorney General: Who was this friend?

Prisoner: A Captain in the army. One who subsequently perished in battle.

Attorney General: What was his name?

Prisoner: Beaupuy. Captain Michel Beaupuy.

Solicitor General: You will confirm this spelling of his name? B-E-A-U-P-U-I

Prisoner: No. There should be a 'Y' at the end.

Attorney General: Did you ever discuss military affairs with this officer?

Prisoner: I am not a military man.

Attorney General: Is that the answer you gave when he attempted to seduce you to fight alongside him against Germanic tyranny?

Prisoner: There was no such attempt.

Home Secretary: And if there had been?

Prisoner: As I said, I am not a military man.

Attorney General: Was any other attempt made to recruit you to the revolutionary cause? Perhaps in a capacity more amenable to your retiring, philosophical nature?

Prisoner: None.

Home Secretary: Not even on your return via Paris?

Prisoner: No.

Home Secretary: Then you affirm you met with no one in Paris?

Prisoner: In those days, it was impossible for an English visitor to meet with no one in Paris.

Home Secretary: It is a simple question, sir.

Prisoner: I may have met with one or two deputies in a spirit of youthful inquiry. But I was eager to return home.

Attorney General: And you did not agree to carry letters across the channel?

Prisoner: It would have been no crime, but I did not.

Home Secretary: This is strange, for I cannot help thinking you were sufficiently engaged by what you encountered in France to retain a strong interest in events there, despite your alleged retreat into rural seclusion.

Prisoner: I would not term my interest strong.

Home Secretary: Indeed? Yet I see that among the many books and papers in your library at Alfoxton, which were examined by an officer of the law at my request, there was one published this very year which urged the necessity of rallying round the French government.

Prisoner: It is not possible to derive the true nature of a man from a mere cursory examination of his bookshelves.

Prime Minister: Although it may be observed that such a book is unlikely to have appeared in the library of the late Mr Burke.

Prisoner: In perusing this book, which was an action of little moment to me, I sought information not instruction. It was no act of turpitude.

Attorney General: You will not mind my asking from whom you purchased this book, Mr Wordsworth?

Prisoner: I did not purchase it.

Attorney General: I am glad to hear that you parted with no money in exchange for such nonsense.

Prisoner: It was sent to me by a friend in Bristol.

Home Secretary: In Bristol? What is his name?

Prisoner: It was the publisher of the book himself, Mr James Losh.

Home Secretary: I see.

Attorney General: And was this book sent to you as a gift? Or was it something more in the nature of an encouragement?

Prisoner: I do not understand.

Attorney General: Mr Wordsworth, we know from our inquiries that you had the good fortune to be named beneficiary in the last will & testament of an unfortunate young man who passed his final days in your care. We now wish to establish whether you have schemed to supplement your income by illicit and treacherous means.

Prisoner: Forgive me, but you speak in riddles.

Lord Chancellor: He refers, of course, to your observations of the local country by day and night; all set down in a secret portfolio.

Home Secretary: And your investigation of the local waterways.

Attorney General: Well, sir, what do you say to that? Was the destruction of Bristol your object? Or did you mean to lure several thousand British soldiers from the place where Bonaparte's gunboats will land?

Home Secretary: We await your answer, Mr Wordsworth.

Prisoner: I confess I am speechless. I do not know how you can have placed such an interpretation on activities undertaken with no other motive than a spirit of poetic inquiry.

Attorney General: Poetic inquiry? It is not we who speak in riddles. Explain yourself.

Prisoner: At the time of which you speak, my friend was enthused with the idea of composing a piece of verse direct from nature, to be called 'The Brook'. We therefore resolved to study the local rivers, dells and waterfalls. It must be this to which you refer.

Attorney General: You mean to tell us that you pursued these activities solely in order to compose a poem?

Lord Chancellor: A fine alibi.

Home Secretary: Presumably you would be able to produce this verse if required?

Prisoner: Would that were the case, but Coleridge grew skittish, as is his wont, and fell to despising his work before it was half finished. The manuscript is almost certainly destroyed.

Lord Chancellor: Next you will be telling us it was eaten up by his pig.

Attorney General: Mr Wordsworth, you do not expect us to believe that a man who has frequented revolutionary circles in London and consorted with French politicians and army officers – a man who has written a manuscript defending the anarchy of the Jacobins & signed himself a republican – should all of a sudden take up residence in a place coveted by the enemy, and there proceed to chart the coast merely with a view to composing a poem about a brook? It is more probable that you spent the time concocting a scheme to achieve the overthrow of established law and government.

Prisoner: I must protest!

Home Secretary: It is an intention ascribed to you by your own sister, which was fortuitously overheard by a loyal subject.

Prisoner: It is a fabrication.

Prime Minister: Recollect, sir, that you address members of the Privy Council. Do not compound the offence of insulting our credulity by what you now begin to insinuate.

Prisoner: I tell the truth.

Lord Chancellor: Enough dissembling. We demand plain speaking; or things will be the worse for you.

Attorney General: Who is Annette, Mr Wordsworth?

Home Secretary: You turn pale, sir.

Solicitor General: Let it be noted the prisoner turned pale and could not immediately be prevailed upon to answer the question.

Prisoner: But-

Lord Chancellor: Well, who is he? What is his position in the chain of command to the Military Council in Paris?

Attorney General: Was Coleridge on his way to meet him before news of the victory at Camperdown threw your plans into confusion?

Prisoner: I am astounded at the nature of these questions.

Home Secretary: You are surprised we possess knowledge of this name?

Prisoner: More so that you consider it to belong to a man.

Attorney General: Come, Mr Wordsworth, we are not unfamiliar with such ruses. I would give little away if I said we regularly receive information from one across the channel who goes by the name of Esther.

Prisoner: There can be nothing in the letters you have evidently seen -

Lord Chancellor: I trust you do not intend to pass these off as billets-doux?

Prisoner: What else could they be?

Attorney General: Why, pieces of traitorous communication.

Prisoner: But they are all dated some years ago.

Home Secretary: These dates cannot be taken at face value.

Prisoner: I tell you, you are mistaken. This is a matter of no concern to any man other than myself.

Lord Chancellor: You would do better to tell us his name.

Attorney General: What about several other members of your acquaintance, Mr Wordsworth? What about Lennox, Wallace and Lacy?

Prisoner: But – how you did you obtain these names?

Attorney General: That is of no concern to you.

Prisoner: They are characters in a play I have penned.

Home Secretary: These men exist, there can be no doubt of that.

Prisoner: I assure you, I submitted the script to Mr Sheridan. I was invited to London at his request to discuss the prospect of its performance.

Attorney General: Doubtless this is what you meant to be understood if you were overheard whispering of your intent to perpetrate a dramatic act.

Prisoner: But Mr Sheridan himself will confirm -

Home Secretary: This would be the same Mr Sheridan who, three years ago, declared the Prime Minister a traitor for suspending habeas corpus and said he deserved to lose his head on the scaffold? I look forward to his corroboration of your story.

Attorney General: Tell us, Mr Wordsworth, how far did you and Coleridge proceed in your scheme to visit the continent by way of Hamburg?

Prisoner: Hamburg?

Attorney General: You do not deny that you intended to go there?

Prisoner: I do not deny that my friend thought there was much benefit to be had from such an expedition.

Attorney General: With whom did you intend to meet?

Prisoner: I scarcely know.

Home Secretary: Then what benefits did your friend seek to obtain from this visit?

Prisoner: I must presume he anticipated a fruitful exchange of ideas.

Attorney General: You mean the opportunity to proliferate a knowledge of your devious code among United Irish spies there?

Prisoner: I speak of philosophical ideas. I know nothing of spies or codes.

Lord Chancellor: We already understand your brand of philosophy, sir. And what it urges.

Attorney General: I suppose you mean to deny the existence of a cipher borne west along the coast by Coleridge to an assignation with a French agent.

Prisoner: I beg your pardon?

Attorney General: You do not recognise this piece of writing?

Solicitor General: Let it be noted the prisoner was shown the paper found in the possession of Samuel Coleridge on his journey west along the coast.

Prisoner: I have never seen this before in my life.

Home Secretary: Come, sir, you mean to divert us with stories of poems that never existed; and then to deny knowledge of those which are presented before your very eyes?

Prisoner: I say again, I have never seen this before in my life.

Attorney General: But, with your more intimate knowledge of the author, you might perhaps be able to elucidate its meaning?

Prisoner: Whoever wrote this, I can only say it appears to be a piece of nonsense rhyme.

Attorney General: You note that it concludes with the word 'war', despite this having little relation to what goes before?

Prisoner: That is in keeping with my previous observation.

Lord Chancellor: We have good reason to believe it is nothing of the sort.

Prisoner: But–

Attorney General: It is a coded communication, is it not? Artfully disguised as literary endeavour – not unlike certain other of your activities – which, when read in conjunction with a book found in your library, would alert those in possession of the cipher to a particular rendezvous for an enemy force.

Prisoner. Impossible.

Home Secretary: Furthermore, its main subjects are 'Khan' and 'water' which, when the latter is translated back into French, provides the identity of the ultimate recipient: 'Khan' and 'eau'. Or M. Carnot, the very man in Paris responsible for directing the enemy war effort at the time this code was devised.

Lord Chancellor: Well, what do you say to that?

Prisoner: I – I confess I am astounded. This can be nothing more than a freakish coincidence. I refuse to countenance the notion that Coleridge was in communication with the enemy.

Attorney General: Indeed, Mr Wordsworth. Perhaps it is not out of the question that you have been the innocent dupe of his schemes?

Home Secretary: You would do well to think on it. For your complicity in an attempt to levy war against His Majesty places you in a most unenviable position.

Lord Chancellor: One that will make you wish you had complied with us from the start.

Prisoner: Gentlemen, that is enough. The questions I have been asked here today are nothing short of preposterous. I demand my immediate release from captivity. The proceedings of this inquiry institute the very -

Solicitor General: Let it be noted the prisoner was escorted from the chamber, pending examination of the other parties concerned.

Extract from the Journal of the Duke of Portland, Wednesday 29th November 1797

No one is persuaded by Wordsworth's protestations of innocence.

Loughborough maintains this to be as arrant a piece of treachery as has been seen these past fifty years. Even the old treason laws would have sufficed.

Yet we are to proceed with caution. An acquittal would be seized upon by our enemies at home and abroad as an invitation to do their worst. It was Coleridge who was found in possession of traitorous correspondence. And the case against him would be overwhelming if it were supplemented by the testimony of a collaborator.

Assuming Wordsworth fears Coleridge to be skittish and unpredictable, he must be terrified his friend will turn King's Evidence against him to save his own skin. Accordingly, there is every chance he shall do the same first.

Record of a Conversation between the Attorney General & Mr Sheridan, MP, which took place 1st December 1797

The ATTORNEY GENERAL thanked Mr Sheridan for hastening to respond to his invitation. He realised his time must be greatly taken up with commissioning new dramatic acts and wished to detain him no longer than absolutely necessary. He simply desired to know whether the name Wordsworth meant anything to him.

Mr SHERIDAN said he did not mean to appear evasive, but as this inquiry came from the Attorney General, he believed it right to know the reason for it.

The ATTORNEY GENERAL replied this was the name of a man presently confined on suspicion of treason who had named Mr Sheridan as one who might exonerate him.

Mr SHERIDAN answered he did not know how, for the life of him.

The ATTORNEY GENERAL stated this prisoner had been found in possession of a list of names which he claimed to be nothing more than a list of characters from a play entitled 'The Borderers' set in medieval Scotland. During his appearance before the Privy Council, he had sworn he submitted this play for the consideration of Mr Sheridan in London. However, the government had good reason to believe it detailed the identities of other conspirators at large in the country.

Mr SHERIDAN replied that, while he did not mean to be circumspect, he reviewed a great many scripts each week. It was not possible to recall the half of them.

The ATTORNEY GENERAL observed that these men had gone to elaborate lengths to conceal their schemes behind a façade of literary endeavour. Mr Sheridan should not be concerned that a correspondence with one of them might imply any broader complicity in their schemes; no matter what his record of opposition to the Government. The sole purpose of this informal discussion was to establish Mr Wordsworth's true intent in undertaking a recent journey to the capital.

Mr SHERIDAN said that, while he could not be sure whether he had corresponded with the prisoner, his work sounded to be greatly detached from the present tastes of the public. It was therefore not probable he had encouraged him to think his play might be staged any time soon.

The ATTORNEY GENERAL inquired whether Mr Sheridan possessed any record of his correspondence with Mr Wordsworth, and if so, whether he would be prepared to testify in court that there was sufficient hope of 'The Borderers' being staged to merit Mr Wordsworth's sudden expedition to London in the middle of winter.

Mr SHERIDAN replied in the negative on both accounts.

Extract from the 'Gentleman's Magazine', December 1797

Mr Watson and Mr Hay, managers of the *Leicester* and *Worcester* Theatres, have set a spirited example to the managers of every similar undertaking throughout the kingdom, by allotting the first and last nights of the season to the support of the State.

Memorandum from John King to the Duke of Portland, Friday 1st December 1797

I write to assure Your Grace that, contrary to our prior understanding, the other suspect in Edinburgh, <u>Thomas Lennox</u>, has been detained upon suspicion of manufacturing pike-heads with intent to arm an insurrectionary force.

Under repeated examination by local magistrates, he has denied all knowledge of Daniel Wallace and of the priest reputed to have supplied him with books. He also insists he is not a member of the United Scotsmen.

He does not deny attending a private lecture at which copies of the 'Rights of Man' were distributed. But he says he did not accept one as he cannot read. He claims to know nothing of parliaments or constitutions; all he has ever sought is a fair wage to feed his family. On this subject, he alleges that his employer is colluding to profiteer from a restriction in the supply of oatmeal in the event of a bad harvest.

Given the lack of progress in interrogating this man, I would know whether it is Your Grace's desire he be transported south to appear in person before the Privy Council.

PS – Every consideration is given to reforming our arrangements in Edinburgh forthwith, including the despatch of a more reliable man.

Letter from Mrs Anna St. Albyn, relict of the Reverend Lancelot St. Albyn, to John Bartholomew Esq., Saturday 2nd December 1797

Sir

Your decision to grant the tenancy of Alfoxton House to a man who stands accused of conspiring to bring the French over betrays a want of judgment which has sullied my family's good name & brought the utmost danger to these shores.

I cannot be satisfied at your defence that you took what Thomas Poole chose to tell you on trust; nor at your explanation that you were anxious to secure a tenant who would do no damage to the house and furniture, as opposed to a large family with careless servants.

I further note that you permitted Thomas Poole to draw up an agreement between you & this vile Jacobin, such that you committed to discharge every rate & tax: all for a nominal sum of just £24 *per annum* to include the house, furniture, gardens, stables & coach-house. <u>I need hardly remind you that we speak here of a gentleman's seat with *nine* lodging rooms.</u>

It was my desire that Alfoxton be inhabited for the remaining minority of my great-nephew. You were entrusted to enter into arrangements to this end. However, it is greatly to be regretted that you did not select to consult with me prior to arriving at your decision.

After going into the matter thoroughly, I find I have no choice but to deprive you of all powers vested in you to act as the agent of my family in matters pertaining to property; and to require your departure from your current place of dwelling, which is to be effected with all possible expedition.

Transcript of the appearance of Samuel Taylor Coleridge before the Board of Interrogation of the Privy Council, 4th December 1797

Among those in attendance:

The Prime Minister
His Grace the Duke of Portland, Home Secretary
The Lord Chancellor, Lord Loughborough
Sir John Scott, Attorney General
Sir John Mitford, Solicitor General
The Prisoner

***

Attorney General: Do you confirm that you are Samuel Coleridge of Lime Street, Nether Stowey, in the county of Somerset?

Prisoner: I have no reason to deny it.

Attorney General: And you have always gone by that name?

Prisoner: My friends address me simply as Coleridge.

Home Secretary: Then the name Silas Tomkyn Comberbache means nothing to you?

Lord Chancellor: Well, sir?

Prisoner: I confess it is a name I formerly adopted some years ago.

Attorney General: Under what circumstances?

Prisoner: In a time of great desperation, when I resolved to join the army.

Attorney General: When exactly was this?

Prisoner: I cannot be sure, for I was in a state of some confusion. But I believe it must have been late in the year 1793.

Prime Minister: I would not term the plight of the nation at that time desperate.

Prisoner: I did not refer to the plight of the nation, so much as to my own. I was scarcely capable of rational thought.

Home Secretary: You mean to say that it was not rational for an Englishman to want to serve his country upon the outbreak of war?

Prisoner: I only mean to say that I was not in my right mind. Hence my discharge after only a few months.

Home Secretary: Your state of mind cannot have been any great impediment, or you would not have endured one week. Whereas you contrived to pass four months obtaining familiarity with the drills and tactics of the militia before your condition became apparent.

Prisoner: It is four months I would gladly forget.

Lord Chancellor: So long as it is not four months you would gladly have us forget.

Home Secretary: The fact remains that you possess significant knowledge of the forces responsible for defending this nation's shores; knowledge which you obtained under an assumed name immediately upon the outbreak of war with France.

Attorney General: Nor have you since volunteered to deploy this knowledge to the benefit of your country, even under the threat of imminent invasion. Instead you chose to scandalise your neighbours with public celebration of Bonaparte's victories on the Italian peninsula.

Prisoner: That is only evidence of my sincere belief in the cause of a united Italy.

Attorney General: We are not here to debate the formation of nation states, Mr Coleridge, but to ascertain the precise nature of your disposition toward your own country.

Prisoner: I assure you, I am nothing but a true patriot.

Home Secretary: That would be reassuring to hear, were it not also the description you applied on a previous occasion to men who desired to plunge the country into anarchy by summoning a Jacobin convention. Men whom it was ultimately considered needful to remove to Botany Bay.

Prisoner: It is not beyond question these men loved their country as much as anyone here present. Several of them have perished for it since, as nobly as any soldier.

Prime Minister: There can be no nobility in treason.

Prisoner: All men know these martyrs were never convicted of treason.

Attorney General: That is by the by, Mr Coleridge. You must curb this tendency for harping on matters not at issue. Answer the questions put to you, concisely and without subterfuge.

Prisoner: I have answered every question put to me. If there is fault to be apportioned for the dilatory nature of these proceedings, it does not lie with me.

Attorney General: Then tell us, without further ado, why a man who, from his earliest days at Cambridge, has fraternised with blasphemers and Jacobins – a man who has set out to provoke disorder with his lectures and sixpenny pamphlets – should all of a sudden retire to a secluded rural life beneath the Quantock Hills?

Prisoner: Have you no powers of imagining? Why do you think, when as things stand a man might be hanged and disembowelled for outwardly contemplating the end of this accursed ministry?

Attorney General: You admit that your political opinions have undergone no review, even in this time of extremity?

Prisoner: I did not say that. The plain truth is that I was greatly fatigued with my former existence. I did not care to teach or write for a newspaper. I thus resolved to learn something of agriculture. It was my ambition to support my family in a state of self-sufficiency on an acre or two of land.

Home Secretary: Perhaps you lost your appetite for penmanship after the failure of your reprehensible journal, *The Watchman*?

Prisoner: It was not a financial success, I admit.

Attorney General: And yet, since arriving at Nether Stowey, you have not devoted your entire energies to agricultural endeavour?

Prisoner: I could not be expected to secede altogether from a life of philosophical contemplation. But I have made it no secret I would rather be an expert self-maintaining gardener than a Milton.

Home Secretary: One would only expect you to have made it a secret if the opposite were true and you aspired to be poet and regicide.

Attorney General: You have frequently been observed to maintain a light in your cottage long after midnight?

Prisoner: That is the only time available for me to undertake valued correspondence.

Lord Chancellor: With the notorious felon, John Thelwall, who stood trial for treason back in '94?

Prisoner: I was not aware he had been found guilty of any crime.

Attorney General: But you do not deny that, in collaboration with one William Wordsworth of Alfoxton House, close by the village of Holford, you undertook to survey the surrounding country, recording your observations in a portfolio?

Prisoner: I have no reason to deny it.

Home Secretary: And you expected reward?

Prisoner: We aspired to reward; we did not expect it.

Attorney General: So when you asked a local man, one Christopher Trickie, whether the nearby brook was navigable to the sea, what was the purpose of this inquiry?

Prisoner: I envisaged the composition of a poem.

Prime Minister: Its navigability was central to your theme?

Prisoner: It was more in the manner of an incidental inquiry, born of natural curiosity.

Attorney General: I take it you would be able to produce this work if required?

Prisoner: Alas, it was never finished.

Attorney General: But doubtless others witnessed it in preparation? Mr Wordsworth, for instance?

Prisoner: Yes.

Attorney General: How long have you known this man, Wordsworth?

Prisoner: I could not tell you precisely. He says we first met in London, but I do not recall it. We were introduced through mutual friends in Bristol and our acquaintance grew from there.

Attorney General: So you must have been delighted when he secured the lease of Alfoxton?

Prisoner: I was.

Attorney General: And your cottage being on the furthest edge of Nether Stowey, this facilitated the arrangement of secret meetings between the two of you?

Prisoner: We had no occasion for secrecy, as you must realise from the nature of the tales carried to you.

Home Secretary: Come, let us waste no more time, sir. We have ascertained you contrived to obtain covert knowledge of the militia under false pretences. Your wild Jacobin views are well known and it is equally transparent that they have undergone no modification. Now, in collaboration with this man Wordsworth – who has all but admitted the fact himself – you conspired to profit in every way possible from charting a place coveted by the enemy, only seeking to obscure your diabolical intentions behind a masquerade of literary endeavour and a rudimentary grasp of crop rotation.

Lord Chancellor: What do you say to that, sir?

Prisoner: What do you expect me to say? It is arrant nonsense. If these accusations were taken to trial, they would be laughed out of court.

Prime Minister: Let us hope you do not live to regret such complacency.

Prisoner: I have not seen or heard one piece of evidence worthy of rousing the militia to secure my person, let alone to empanel a jury.

Attorney General: Very well, then. Doubtless you will be able to account for the words set down on this paper?

Solicitor General: Let it be noted the prisoner was shown the message discovered about his person during his solitary progress west along the coast on Friday 13th October.

Prisoner: But – how did you obtain this?

Lord Chancellor: You seem aghast?

Prisoner: I am shocked to find it in your possession.

Home Secretary: You admit you would not readily have parted with it?

Prisoner: In truth, I recollect little of the journey you describe, having had recourse to opiates to check a dysentery.

Prime Minister: A not inconvenient lapse of memory, it must be observed.

Attorney General: But you do not deny familiarity with the words in question?

Prisoner: I scarcely know what to say.

Home Secretary: If they are the device of somebody else, you would be well advised to inform us.

Prisoner: I tell you, I do not know. I cannot account for their composition, nor how they came to be in your possession. But surely they are of no interest to the Privy Council?

Attorney General: Why do you say that?

Prisoner: These words constitute nothing but nonsense rhyme. There is an underlying theme of fecundity, perhaps. And a certain hypnotic effect which is not displeasing to the ear, but -

Home Secretary: You were seen to have recourse to a spyglass to observe vessels in the Bristol Channel. Whom did you purpose to meet?

Prisoner: I had no intention of meeting anyone. I sought solitude; solitude and inspiration.

Attorney General: Then you were not asked to convey a message thither?

Prisoner: A message? What sort of message?

Lord Chancellor: Why, a coded message. One urging the enemy to land an armed force; its object the destruction of Bristol.

Prisoner: What new fantasy is this?

Home Secretary: It is no fantasy. We have it on good authority from those who make the deciphering of codes their constant study that, in combination with a book to be found in the library at Alfoxton, this alleged nonsense rhyme identifies a rendezvous for a French landing force.

Prisoner: Impossible. How could it do that?

Attorney General: The purpose of this session is for us to examine you, not the reverse. You will find out soon enough.

Prime Minister: Wait a moment. Might it not be advantageous to hear what the prisoner says to refute the interpretation placed upon this cipher?

Solicitor General: Let it be recorded the Board of Interrogation temporarily withdrew from the chamber. The prisoner remained confined in his place. The session was then reconvened.

Attorney General: We observe you do not deny authorship of this document; nor that you bore it with you on your unaccountable expedition west of Minehead?

Prisoner: As I have told you already, my recollection of much of that journey is nothing but a dream.

Attorney General: None the less, you would concur that these lines derive from an obscure travel book, a copy of which was to be found in the library at Mr Wordsworth's property?

Prisoner: I would.

Attorney General: Then perhaps you would care to explain why the measurements supplied by the author of those travels differ so greatly from the ones specified in this verse?

Prisoner: I beg your pardon?

Home Secretary: Why does the Khan's palace encompass not sixteen miles, but ten? Are we to infer that in the intervening period he has sold off part of his estate?

Prisoner: Allow me to consult the rhyme a moment. Why, the measurement you refer to is not ten, but twice five. Gentlemen, this alteration is made for poetic effect.

Attorney General: Poetic effect? Is that also your explanation for entitling the river Alph, when it has no name in the travel book?

Prisoner: I conceive this to be an allusion to Alpheus, thereby associating the river with the muse of pastoral poetry as cited in Milton's *Lycidas*.

Prime Minister: Your explanations come pat to hand for one who could scarcely account for the composition of these lines a few moments ago.

Home Secretary: I thought you had claimed you would rather be a self-maintaining gardener than another Milton?

Prisoner: The fact is, all these changes, whose fascination to you I make no attempt to fathom, are explicable on grounds of poetic effect.

Home Secretary: You speak your opinion, sir, not fact. It does not contradict the one indisputable truth: that these changes were effected.

Attorney General: You do not deny, I suppose, that the principal subjects of this verse are Khan and water: which, when the latter is rendered into French, become Khan and 'eau'. Or Monsieur Carnot, the man in charge of the enemy war effort at the time this cipher was devised?

Prisoner: You do not think that you can persuade a jury of free-born Englishmen -

Attorney General: On the contrary, the challenge of persuading them will be yours, sir.

Home Secretary: Are we to infer that the inspiration for employing verse in this manner came from your own lectures on the "revolutionary power" of literature?

Attorney General: Perhaps it was your intention to make for Hamburg, there to align yourself with United Irish spies in anticipation of a Spring offensive by Bonaparte?

Lord Chancellor: Is that where Wallace is gone?

Prisoner: Wallace? Who is Wallace?

[Page or pages missing]

Extract from the Notebooks of George Heaton

(Subsequently Deciphered)

Evening at tavern in Lambeth.

Approached by aged crone worse for liquor. Offered to sell me lock of C's hair. Entirely wrong hue.

Subscription raised by 'Friends of Liberty' to pay W & C legal expenses?

***

Beset with fear as to consequences of trial.

Name & description published abroad as government spy. What then?

Memorandum from John King to the Duke of Portland, Tuesday 5th December 1797

Further to Your Grace's instruction, the packet of letters bearing the signature 'Annette' has been transported to London under armed guard and scrutinised by Maddison.

No evidence of a secret code could be found. It would seem these letters may be exactly what they appear: namely passionate *billets-doux* sent to Wordsworth by a mistress who, as a result of their liaison, became mother to his child.

Such conclusions are preliminary in nature and may remark nothing beside the extreme deviousness of the codes employed by these men.

But even if these letters be genuine, they raise considerable doubt as to Wordsworth's loyalties, since he evidently possessed much incentive to conspire with M. Carnot, in addition to that derived from his staunch Jacobin convictions.

PS – I take the liberty of submitting for Your Grace's consideration a thought which has occurred to me concerning the French army captain named by Wordsworth. As Your Grace will recall, this man's name was Beaupuy, or as pronounced in English Bo-P. I could not help but be struck by the similarity between this and the name BonaParte.

Report Submitted to His Majesty's Government Upon A Monstrous Alliance between Thomas Paine & Napoleon Bonaparte, December 1797

The man with the red carbuncled face and black eyes, whom Bonaparte has received at dinner, is none other than Thomas Paine, author of 'Rights of Man' and inspirer of revolution in the American colonies.

This Paine has drawn up an elaborate document, complete with maps and charts, entitled *Observations on the Construction & Operation of Navies with a Plan for an Invasion of England and the Final Overthrow of the English Government.*

He conceives a scheme for raising ten million livres to build and equip a fleet of gunboats. With this, he means to land a force of ten-thousand troops which, he proclaims, will soon be joined by legions of local men who are great friends to the cause of liberty.

Bonaparte has seduced Paine with arrant flattery. He declares that he sleeps with a copy of the 'Rights of Man' beneath his pillow. And he has promised that a statue of its author will be mounted on a plinth in a fine new square in the heart of London. He says Paine must be allowed to accompany an invasion force, and shall assume the position of leader of a provisional English revolutionary government as soon as is practicable.

Efforts have commenced to undermine this monstrous alliance by provoking those tensions as shall inevitably result from the frequent intercourse of two such egotists. Steps have been taken to inculcate a belief among people of consequence that Paine is an ingenious double-agent; and that his plan for a maritime descent upon Britain is nothing but a sly scheme to lure Bonaparte and his army to a watery grave. The Minister of General Police is known to be susceptible to such suspicions. It is hoped he may be encouraged to have Paine arrested and interrogated; an act which, it is intended, shall sew the seeds of doubt in Bonaparte's mind and force him to think twice before pursuing this vile invasion plan.

Letter from John Poole, Fellow of Oriel College, Oxford, to His Grace the Duke of Portland, Thursday 7th December 1797

It is with the greatest veneration, and after much consultation with the Fellowship of this College, which I trust is not without friends among His Majesty's Ministers, that I beseech Your Grace to exhibit the utmost restraint in the case of my cousin, Thomas Poole, who was recently summoned before the Privy Council to give an account of his association with one Samuel Coleridge.

My cousin is a man of worth and substance, much admired for his charitable works. He is not wanting in those of standing willing to testify as to his character. I am persuaded it is this, his generous good nature, sheltered as it has been by an existence passed too much in isolation save for the company of his invalid mother, that has betrayed him into a misguided beneficence toward the man Coleridge, little knowing that he clutched a viper to his bosom.

I fear my cousin fancied himself a patron of the arts and unwisely conceived he might temper Coleridge's vile politicking by persuading him to renounce it in favour of that art to which his faculties were more suited; namely poesy. In this, he was shamelessly led on by this scurrilous gadfly, who schemed to use my cousin's good name to conceal his own perfidious machinations. I conceive he may have set his mind to this from the very first day he visited Nether Stowey, when he came in the company of one Robert Southey, against whom I likewise counsel Your Grace, for these men were equals in depravity.

I trust that, whatever evidence may be held against Coleridge, no suspicion shall attach to my cousin. I look forward to the day when he is restored to the bosom of his family which, I assure Your Grace, will do all within its power to ensure his ardent generosity of spirit is never again the victim of such cruel and treacherous duplicity.

I remain, Your Grace's most humble & obedient servant.

Letter from Samuel Coleridge to the Duke of Portland, Thursday 14th December 1797

I desire to know how much longer it will be Your Grace's pleasure to keep me confined in this place.

Consider that, in the very depths of winter, I am held in a tiny cell with neither glass in the casement, nor a fire to keep me warm; so much so, that my legs grow ulcerated with the frost. All this time, I have been denied the solace of books & the consolation of society beyond that which I might obtain through bars.

Consider also that I am not without friends. Not least, those sacred liberties enshrined these many centuries past, which entitle me to bring a writ of unlawful detention against my captors and to seek recompense in proportion to my suffering.

Know that I hereby serve notice of my intention to do so, if I am not released forthwith and granted safe passage to my wife & child; in order that we may resume our lawful existence in accordance with the right of every free-born Englishman.

Memorandum from John King to the Duke of Portland, Monday 18th December 1797

I regret to inform Your Grace that no argument yet persuades Wordsworth to turn King's evidence against Coleridge:

- not the assurance, freely given, that he will obtain amnesty for his sister;

- not the overt picturing of that fate suffered by Jacobite traitors fifty years ago, whose bowels were cast into the flames before their dying eyes;

- not the intimation that Coleridge, desperate to save himself, makes ready to accuse him of composing the nonsense rhyme and commissioning its carriage west along the coast to an assignation with the enemy;

As for Wordsworth's sister, she remains confined to Bedlam. But we have this day received an appeal from her eldest brother, Richard Wordsworth Esq, to sanction her removal to a remote place, where she might receive proper attention without further encumbrance to the nation.

NB – I conceive this appeal to be calculated upon a presumption she is no Joan of Arc, and that, in her current condition, she can be of no utility as a witness and may only arouse pity for the defendants.

Extract from the Journal of the Duke of Portland, Tuesday 19th December 1797

I cannot say why, but Mr Pitt is suddenly reluctant to prosecute this case with full vigour. This evening he invited me to Downing Street to inquire if the object of the Privy Council meeting might not be <u>whether</u> to indict rather than whom.

When I asked what he meant by this, he declared: 'Why, another suspension of habeas corpus, that these reprobates might be held for an indefinite period, where they can do no harm!'

Certainly his health is not what it was. At times his face resembles a fox at bay, only calculating how to parry while his remaining strength endures. Tonight he had frequent recourse to a medicinal flask.

Is he grown over-weary with the cares of office? Or does he manoeuvre to abolish the Alien Office, supplant me, and then take credit himself for destroying our enemies within these shores?

<u>We must proceed to indictment</u>. A suspension of habeas corpus would leave us open to the charge that we attack those very liberties we seek to uphold. And the evidence against these men is strong. If Coleridge were left to linger in Cold Bath Fields and the place stormed by enemy troops, what horrors might we not expect from a mob led by this man through the smouldering ruins of London?

Extract from the 'Gentleman's Magazine', December 1797

On consideration of the various reports of the Finance Committee, the Board of Treasury has determined to adopt the most scrupulous economy in every department of public expenditure, by abolishing all useless offices as they fall vacant.

Minutes of a Privy Council Committee, summoned the 20th day of December 1797, To Determine Whether to Proceed to Indictment in the Instance of the Late Treachery at Nether Stowey

The PRIME MINISTER declared that, all present having had time to consider the answers given by each of the principal suspects before the Board of Interrogation, it was now imperative to formulate a means of proceeding. Before that, he wished to commend the Home Secretary on the achievement of his office in combating the loathsome act which some or all of these men had appeared to contemplate.

The HOME SECRETARY thanked the Prime Minister for this sentiment. He understood the Attorney General had given consideration to drafting a bill of indictment, and was confident the traitors could be brought to justice before the onset of Spring.

The PRIME MINISTER said he did not doubt this, but that he must impress upon all present the necessity of ensuring a conviction. Otherwise a trial might achieve the opposite of what was intended and deal a fatal blow to the Government, just when the nation could least afford it. It might even prove the incendiary spark for a Jacobin uprising accompanied by the assault of a French fleet. In short, unless a guilty verdict could be depended upon – and he knew he spoke for the remainder of His Majesty's Ministers in urging this – he must advocate a different course of action; namely the suspension of *habeas corpus*.

This would permit the prisoners to be held indefinitely, and allow the government to concentrate its energies on repelling Bonaparte's invasion.

The LORD CHANCELLOR declared that he saw no argument for a suspension of *habeas corpus*. The evidence against these men was incontrovertible. Proceeding to indictment represented the best method of deterring other traitors, who would see their own fate writ large in the decomposing heads of these felons.

The HOME SECRETARY observed that suspending *habeas corpus* would leave them open to the charge they assaulted the very liberties they claimed to protect.

The ATTORNEY GENERAL said it must be difficult to overlook the fact these men had brooded the murder of each man present.

The PRIME MINISTER replied that, none the less, they must consider the position in which the country found itself. It was no exaggeration to state that what depended upon this trial was not just the future of His Majesty's Government, but the nation also.

The HOME SECRETARY suggested that the matter could only be determined with reference to each prisoner in turn.

The LORD CHANCELLOR concurred. He had not encountered any difficulty in forming an opinion as to the culpability of each man. He did not see why an appropriately constituted jury might not be depended upon to do the same.

Whether to Proceed to Indictment in the Case of Miss Wordsworth:

The HOME SECRETARY proposed first to resolve that decision which ought to be most elementary, namely the case of Wordsworth's sister. This woman had suffered a precipitous descent into madness upon her arrest and had not recovered her wits. It was beyond dispute she had been cognisant of these men's ambitions and had accompanied them in their observations of the surrounding country. But her fitness to participate in legal proceedings was wholly diminished, and her presence in court might well exercise an undesirable effect upon a jury. It was his recommendation that the Privy Council move to accept a solicitation from her family; namely that she be removed at their expense to a remote location and confined under the regimen of a respectable physician.

The PRIME MINISTER inquired whether she had been heard to utter anything incriminating, notwithstanding the alleged disturbance to her mind.

The HOME SECRETARY replied in the negative.

The COMMITTEE concluded by unanimous vote to pursue the Home Secretary's recommendation, stipulating only that His Majesty's Ministers be notified of any alteration in Miss Wordsworth's condition or place of residence by the physician in attendance.

*Whether to Proceed to Indictment in the Case of
Thomas Poole:*

The HOME SECRETARY observed that the appearance
of Thomas Poole before the Board of Interrogation
had yielded little of note. While he had confessed to
circulating copies of the 'Rights of Man' and to promoting
a Society of Poor Men, the evidence against him was not
all it could be.

The PRIME MINISTER agreed, stating that, upon careful
reflection, he believed Poole to be guilty of nothing but
monumental folly.

The ATTORNEY GENERAL added that, while it was
difficult to conceive Poole had been entirely ignorant
of Coleridge's disposition, no hoard of weapons had
been discovered to prove the existence of a Poor Man's
army.

The LORD CHANCELLOR countered these arguments,
stating that patronage of these men was itself enough
to damn the prisoner in question. The nation could do
without such dangerously well-intentioned men.

A vote was taken and all present agreed that Thomas
Poole should not be indicted, save for the LORD
CHANCELLOR who chose to abstain.

*Whether to Proceed to Indictment in the Case of
William Wordsworth:*

The HOME SECRETARY observed that the evidence
against the next prisoner was of an altogether more

compelling nature. The desire of William Wordsworth to achieve the overthrow of established law and government had been conclusively established. It was clear he had nourished traitorous ambitions ever since his first visit to France.

The PRIME MINISTER asked what had been the prisoner's response to the proposition he turn King's Evidence in exchange for his life.

The HOME SECRETARY indicated that this had been greeted with disdain.

The PRIME MINISTER said he regretted this, for he was afraid the circumstantial nature of the case against Wordsworth might be dismantled by a competent attorney.

The ATTORNEY GENERAL declared that, while he would prefer to be summoning Wordsworth as a witness for the prosecution, he was inclined to think any jury cognisant of the man's character and disposition must be minded to convict. The evidence against him might be likened to a Roman mosaic, wherein fragmentary and indeterminate pieces together constituted a picture most clear.

The PRIME MINISTER noted that a majority appeared in favour of indictment. He requested that, since this was contrary to his previous determination, the discussion should proceed to Coleridge before a final decision was taken.

Whether to Proceed to Indictment in the Case of
Samuel Coleridge:

The HOME SECRETARY declared the case against Coleridge to be irrefutable. The man's conduct since the outbreak of war was sufficient to condemn him. And it was on his person the traitorous correspondence had been discovered.

The LORD CHANCELLOR asserted that the government would look downright cowardly, if it did not proceed to indictment.

The ATTORNEY GENERAL concurred that a guilty verdict was assured.

The PRIME MINISTER said it was none the less his duty to remind them what depended on this trial. They must be certain there was no impediment to conviction.

The ATTORNEY GENERAL inquired whether there was any impediment to conviction arising from the need to protect an informant.

The HOME SECRETARY said that the gravity of the case justified the appearance in court of the agent in question, even if this did compromise his identity. He would later be found employment in a distant sphere.

The PRIME MINISTER owned that, for his part, he believed Coleridge to be guilty. Furthermore, Wordsworth's character and disposition were indubitably blackened by his obstinate refusal to turn King's Evidence. It was difficult not to conclude these men had entered into a diabolical collaboration. Moreover, he trusted he now had full assurance that a guilty verdict might be depended upon.

A vote was taken to charge Samuel Taylor Coleridge, of Lime Street, Nether Stowey, and his accomplice William Wordsworth, lately tenant of Alfoxton House, in the county of Somerset, with High Treason. This was passed without dissent.

Matters Arising:

The ATTORNEY GENERAL undertook to draw up a bill of indictment against the prisoners, and to enter into formalities concerning the release of Thomas Poole and the confinement of Miss Wordsworth under the supervision of a suitable physician. He also undertook to secure the release of two men, presently held at Bridgwater, upon suspicion of swearing a secret oath and concealing arms for a malign & traitorous purpose.

Fragment of verse composed by William Wordsworth during his confinement

The thick-ribbed walls that o'ershadow the gate
Resound; and the dungeons unfold:
I pause; and at length, through the glimmering grate
That outcast of pity behold.

His black matted head on his bosom is bent,
And deep is the sigh of his breath,
While with steadfast dejection his eye is intent
On the fetters that link him to death.

Letter from Richard Wordsworth to the Duke of Portland, Thursday 28th December 1797

I write to convey my most humble and fervent gratitude at Your Grace's decision to permit the removal of my sister from her most recent place of habitation.

I trust Your Grace is fully satisfied by the arrangements notified to Mr King; both as to her intended place of convalescence & the most dependable personage under whose ministration she will be placed.

I remain, Your Grace's most humble and obedient servant,

Extract from a Memorandum to the Prime Minister from the Attorney General, copied to the Home Secretary, Friday 5th January 1798

For my part, I consider the abolition of trial by jury in cases of High Treason to be neither requisite nor advisable for the following reasons:-

i. The Bill of Indictment must be heard by the Grand Jury of Middlesex, which is to be constituted from a list of eligible freeholders and certain influential leaseholders, the vast majority of whom exist in violent opposition to the ideas of Thomas Paine and his adherents.

ii. As you know, the summoning of a Grand Jury is fraught with difficulty. You will recall that, before the treason trials three years ago, several men were mistakenly informed their attendance was unnecessary; while others, alas, received a summons the night *after* it was required. I note that the Grand Jury as constituted duly found those accused had a case to answer.

iii. Regarding the trial itself, a list of eligible jurors will be drawn up from a pool of propertied men subject to the usual exemptions: surgeons, apothecaries, clergymen, dissenting teachers, Quakers, etc. But I would remind you that I retain the power to summon a Special Jury, as I have always done in cases of seditious libel, let alone those of an even more serious nature. We shall

> therefore retain the right to review this Jury and to remove up to a quarter of those men presented.

In anticipation of this, I suggest that the Lord Chief Justice's Office circulate the names of the first hundred men in the jury pool to those who might reliably possess knowledge of them. Recipients of this list should identify those men with whom they are familiar and grade them in the margin as follows:

'G' for good man;

'B' for bad man;

'D' for doubtful.

By this means, I conceive it will be feasible to secure a jury consisting of at least eight G's, with all B's absent, and – God willing – all D's.

Memorandum from John King to the Duke of Portland, Thursday 11th January 1798

I write with urgent despatch to inform Your Grace that Heaton has failed to keep an assignation.

The man is obliged to exchange rooms with considerable frequency. But he is punctilious almost to the point of severity. I therefore remain at a loss to account for this sudden disappearance.

One explanation may lie in his unbounded ardour to prove himself of utility; for no decision has yet been reached as to his future & he is still to receive gratuity for his accomplishment at Nether Stowey. It is conceivable he may have made some discovery concerning another conspiracy which precipitated his immediate departure from London, but which did not furnish him with the opportunity to communicate his intended direction.

PS – As requested, I have instituted inquiries to establish the whereabouts of <u>Robert</u> <u>Southey</u>. However, this man's name does not appear in any report received from Somerset; nor in any recent despatch from Hamburg. Is it possible he may have adopted an alias?

Extracts from the Journal of the Duke of Portland, Tuesday 16th January 1798

What are we to make of this calamitous disappearance?

Am I to reproach myself that Heaton has met an untimely end at the hands of some United Irish assassin, or else a friend of Wordsworth? Is he the instrument of his own vanishing, intimidated at the consequences of so public a disclosure of his identity? Does he mean to bargain for greater reward, not knowing how needful it is he stand up in court and swear he has received nothing beyond the satisfaction of serving his country?

Certain it is, I confront a most unenviable dilemma:

If I say he is slain by disease and rapidly interred for fear of contagion, the trial must collapse and Mr Pitt shall have his suspension of habeas corpus.

But if I confess he is disappeared, I shall appear so encumbered with the armoury of legislation, that I scarce know how to wield the sword of justice. Worse still, those who fawn upon the navy must find their arguments irretrievably advanced. So much so, that I cannot help but wonder if the public house where Heaton lingered was purposely found out and visited by a press-gang.

Memorandum from the Attorney General to the Duke of Portland, Thursday 18th January 1798

I hereby confirm that the Grand Jury of Middlesex has convened at Hicks Hall. After due consideration of the indictment, it has determined that both prisoners shall stand trial before a Special Jury, to be empanelled the penultimate day of February.

The names of the first hundred men in the jury pool are now circulated. As a consequence, several persons are already eliminated: of whom I mention, by way of indication, Nathaniel Gosling, a stationer; Edward Townsend, a hatter; and Joseph Ellis, an optician.

PS – I believe it quite necessary to disclose the suspicious observations undertaken at Fishguard prior to the landing of the *Legion Noir*; for this must demonstrate whence came the inspiration for these men to obscure their activities behind a pretence of literary endeavour.

PPS – I would urge the immediate removal of the witness, Heaton, to a place of safety. This man's testimony is of the first consequence & he would benefit from time to prepare it. Counsel for the defence shall assuredly employ all means to destroy his credibility, cast aspersions as to his motives, etc. It is most desirable that he appear an ardent patriot whose conduct derives entirely from an admirable loyalty to His Majesty.

Memorandum from the Attorney General to the Duke of Portland, Monday 29th January 1798

It is now more than a week since I wrote to Your Grace urging removal of the witness, Heaton, to a place of safety. But, I must confess, I had not anticipated so careful a manner of proceeding, that I myself would be denied knowledge of his whereabouts or access to his person.

I would remind Your Grace that the day of the trial approaches. Notwithstanding a laudable resolution to guarantee the safekeeping of this invaluable witness, I must ask that he now be placed at my disposal. It is wholly necessary I prepare his mind for an appearance in court when he will, of a sudden, find himself stood directly opposite the men he accuses.

Memorandum from the Duke of Portland to John King, Tuesday 30th January 1798

I trust you are correct in estimating that Heaton has simply vanished into Kent upon the trail of some new conspiracy. But with each day that passes, I find it more difficult to place a favourable interpretation upon his disappearance, or to dispel anxiety as to its consequences. It seems to me we are just as likely to discover him in a mortuary, or on a packet-boat making for the continent.

While I remain reluctant to furnish abroad a description of his person – even under a false name as if it were that of a fugitive – the situation now merits the hazard of much to locate him. I therefore ask that you let it be known, in a discrete manner, that a most substantial reward shall be paid for the discovery of this man, in a safe condition, before the week is out.

Deposition of Benjamin Jenkyns, Fisherman, of Whitstable in the County of Kent, as to what took place on the afternoon of Friday 2nd February & thereafter

I was at work on my boat when I saw a man, a stranger, standing close by. His hair was cropped & he had eyes like the north sea before a blizzard. He asked about the tides & what weather I was expecting.

Then he said the Lord smiled on me, for he was sent by his master, a man of means, who wished to go to the continent with his servants. He did not use the packet-boat as it did not go where he wanted to go. He said he would pay me 150 guineas and set aside another 300 against my vessel being taken.

I asked where did he want to go.

He said a bay in France; I do not remember which.

I said I was not taking my boat to that ---- country.

He smiled & asked if I would go to Hamburg, or to Holland.

I said Holland.

We made a bargain. He promised to pay me first thing the next morning.

My passenger was Captain Jones. He had a strange accent, but so do many others & I had no suspicion of him; not till he tried to swindle me. He said he would pay me double the sum if I would accept the money when we reached Holland.

I said I would, but only if his bags were first searched by the Excise.

He said he did not like this, but I sent for them all the same.

He kept back two small wood boxes. He said his servants had lost the keys.

The Excise-men said they must see inside the boxes before they would let him go.

He got angry and said he did not see how the keys could be found, so they must all disembark. All five went back to Whitstable. I did not see them again.

They never paid for the catch I went without.

Signed 'X': His Mark

Memorandum from John King to the Duke of Portland, Wednesday 7th February 1798

I hereby confirm that five men suspected of attempting to secure passage to France under false names have been seized at Margate by two constables & a party of light horse.

They were arrested at a public house called The King's Head: a name which, I fear, occupied no ordinary significance in the minds of these men, for they are not the party of military men & servants they purported to be, nor a set of smugglers, but rather a gang of traitorous insurrectionists.

Their <u>true</u> names are:

JOHN BINNS, a secretary of the London Corresponding Society, formerly arrested on a charge of sedition;

JAMES O'COIGLY, an Irish priest, who first claimed his name was Captain Jones, then James Fevey;

ARTHUR O'CONNOR, the proprietor of an Irish newspaper;

JEREMIAH LEARY & JOHN ALLEN, both being servants.

Among their belongings were found:

A purse of Louis D'Ors;
Several charts of the coast;
Daggers & firearms;

A passport, almost destroyed, showing that one of them – I know not which – had formerly been in France;

A message to the French Government, urging the imminent landing of troops.

This last item was found in the top-coat of the priest, O'Coigly, who denies all knowledge of it. But he has practised such deceptions that his character is entirely repudiated. Not only has he sought refuge in several false identities, but his claim to be soliciting passage back to Ireland is contradicted both by witness testament and by the fact that he ventured to depart from a place more convenient for Hamburg than Dublin.

PS – I am told that O'Connor's servant is overcome with fear and treats to turn King's Evidence against his master. He may yet be summoned to appear at more than one trial. For there is good reason to suspect an association between these men and those arrested at Nether Stowey. Indeed it is not beyond question that O'Coigley is the very priest who visited the fugitive watch-maker, Wallace, in Edinburgh.

Record of a Conversation between the Prime Minister & the Home Secretary, Thursday 8th February 1798

The PRIME MINISTER desired to know more of the arrests made on the coast of Kent, for there were contradictory accounts abroad. One suggested that these seven men had been landed by the French as a scouting party; another that this was some new dalliance of the London Corresponding Society with the United Irish, a development which, if true, he must regard with the gravest concern.

The HOME SECRETARY said he could confirm these were five men and they had not been landed by the French, but had sought passage to that country with a secret message urging an invasion. He feared this might well imply a new and deplorable alliance between the London Corresponding Society and the United Irish. But he had always maintained these plots to be Hydra-headed. No sooner was one destroyed, than several more sprang forth in its place.

The PRIME MINISTER inquired if any association had been discovered between these men and the prisoners from Nether Stowey.

The HOME SECRETARY said it had already been observed that Margate existed in relation to London as Nether Stowey did to Bristol. He awaited the arrival of these conspirators in London, that they might be properly examined. In the meanwhile, he considered it advisable to delay the trial of Coleridge and Wordsworth.

The PRIME MINISTER expressed concern that any postponement of this trial would be proclaimed by the Government's opponents as proof it possessed no real evidence against the prisoners. It might also be taken by the wider public as a signal invasion was imminent, thereby provoking scenes of disorder and panic. He wondered if these latest arrests did not confirm a more desirable course lay in the suspension of habeas corpus.

The HOME SECRETARY said that if anything was worthy of suspension, it was only the packet-boat service between Yarmouth & Cuxhaven, the continued operation of which defied sense.

The PRIME MINISTER agreed that this should be looked into. He also owned that conviction of the prisoners in a court of law must exercise a stimulatory effect upon public vigilance. One way to avoid any untoward consequence of a postponement of the trial might be to announce a new date at once.

Matters Arising:

It was resolved to seek the opinion of the Attorney General with a view to delaying the trial of the prisoners from Nether Stowey, pending interrogation by the Privy Council of the five men lately arrested in Kent.

Memorandum from John King to the Duke of Portland, Saturday 10th February 1798

I must inform Your Grace of a most alarming discovery made as a consequence of our continued attention to the person of Coleridge's wife.

As Your Grace will recall, this woman was questioned upon her husband's arrest, but she was not transported to London as she had been observed to be wholly excluded from his activities. None the less, it was decided to watch her progress, for she had expressed the intention of proceeding to Bristol to throw herself upon the mercy of several publishers known to be of dubious allegiance.

Needless to say, this woman's identity as the wife of a suspected traitor was duly found out and her lodgings besieged by a crowd intent upon demonstrating its loyalty to His Majesty. These people were encouraged by neighbours who discovered she was with child and feared she might become an encumbrance upon the parish. The crowd was dispersed, but not before the woman had taken such a fright that she fell down in a faint. Upon her recovery, a local magistrate deemed her presence a threat to public order and instigated proceedings for her removal. She at once sent for the publisher, James Losh, and entrusted him with her meagre savings on condition that he arrange for the conveyance of her young son to her sister in Portugal.

The name of this sister is Mrs <u>Southey</u> and her husband is none other than that very <u>Robert Southey</u> into whose whereabouts Your Grace has formerly inquired. It would seem that this man's presence in the aforementioned country – whose conquest by the enemy would entail the direst consequences for the strategic and commercial interests of this nation – has not been accorded the suspicion it merits.

PS – Mrs Coleridge is by no means desirous of visiting or otherwise communicating with her husband, whom she appears to view as the author of her manifold distresses.

Extract from a Speech to Parliament by William Pitt the Younger, Wednesday 14th February 1798

"What, then, does the Right Honourable Gentleman mean when he advocates conciliation? I say he means this:

"That we should make every concession and every sacrifice to traitors and rebels; to men who are industriously propagating the most dangerous principles, engrafting upon the minds of the people the most destructive doctrines, wantonly seducing and deluding the ignorant multitude, encouraging the most criminal correspondence with the enemy, & exciting the commission of treason.

"But the Government has the clue to the conspiracy in its hands. And it will use all necessary precautions to prevent – and exertions to suppress – the horrible attempts of those who would tear out the vitals of their common mother."

**Extract from the 'Edinburgh Evening Courant',
Saturday 17th February 1798**

It is now known that the *bloody and lifeless corpse* discovered frozen in its death agony in the early hours of Friday morning, is that of Thomas Lennox, aged 46 years.

Several witnesses have presented themselves, no doubt in the expectation of reward, who claim that they heard a *shout of altercation* from the place where the body was found with its throat severed; and that they saw *two men loitering* in the vicinity the previous evening, their features obscured as a result of precaution taken against the severe chill.

But it is the understanding of this publication that the demise of this man, who was lately cast out of employ at a local manufactory of oatmeal, is rather to be explained by the presence of *a knife clasped in his own hand*; and by the fact that, not a day previous, he had confided to a friend that *he found himself in great difficulties* as a result of certain lamentable actions on his own part.

It must be presumed that this Lennox, almost certainly *under the influence of spirituous liquor*, resolved upon the desperate measure of appointing himself *the instrument of his own destruction*.

Memorandum from John King to the Duke of Portland, Monday 19th February 1798

I rejoice to send Your Grace word Heaton is found.

It would appear that the man was visited by a dismal ague and his body wracked with all manner of cramps and palpitations. He could find no means of sending us word, for, having just exchanged lodgings, he dared employ no messenger without fearing to place his person in the gravest danger. In a few hours more, his mind was overtaken by delirium. When this passed off, he was seized by a fearful lassitude which lasted many weeks.

While his body is weak, he is pronounced out of danger. The Attorney General will see him shortly. And I should confirm that he has made no attempt to parlay for greater reward, nor to shy away from the forthcoming trial, which he approaches manfully & with all the resolution one might expect of a patriot whose first determination has always been to protect this nation from its vilest enemies.

PS – I would respectfully suggest that, in a few days more, we acquaint Heaton with the task he is to be allotted beyond the trial. For I conceive this may exercise a further restorative effect upon his mind.

**Extract from the Journal of the Duke of Portland,
Tuesday 20th February 1798**

These rumours that Bonaparte contemplates extending the theatre of war to India are nothing but a perfidious diversion. Hardly a week goes by when Paine does not publish in Paris, quoting Gibbon on the ease with which the Romans conquered this isle & threatening the despatch of ten-thousand men in gunboats.

If the French set sail from Toulon into the Mediterranean, their intention will surely be to double back from that sea & create sufficient havoc in the English Channel to permit these gunboats to make the coast of Kent.

***

To my astonishment, the Archbishop of Canterbury has declared that, were the clergy to accept commissions in the army or be trained in the use of arms, it would interfere with the duties of the profession. Does he mean to imply that a government of Jacobins in London would _not_ interfere with the duties of the profession?

Memorandum from John King to the Duke of Portland, Friday 23rd February 1798

I have today visited O'Coigly, who is made aware that his servant has denounced him.

None the less, he continues to protest his innocence. He says he would never have been so reckless as to write down an invitation to the French to invade. If he had wished to convey such a message, he would have employed the most impenetrable cipher. Accordingly, the letter must have been planted among his baggage. Since he will not condemn his fellow travellers, he implies this was the work of a constable, or some other agent in the employ of the government.

He maintains that he is not a United Irishman, but has from his earliest days sought to act as a peacemaker. He admits that this has taken him into places where there is much seditious talk – Manchester, Nottingham, Sheffield – but he swears that he has not been in Edinburgh. Nor does he know anything of any man there by the name of Wallace;. nor has he ever been in the environs of the Quantock Hills; nor has he heard of any opprobrious activities in that place, etc, etc.

In short, this man is resolved upon martyrdom and means to perish for a cause with which he would have us believe he has no affiliation. There is no reason to think that he will amend this resolution. Accordingly, I see little argument to delay commencement of the trial of Coleridge & Wordsworth beyond the 6th March.

Extract from the Journal of the Duke of Portland, Monday 5th March 1798

Let our enemies contemplate the mighty deterrent which is the operation of English justice. And let those who fawn upon the navy behold the overwhelming requirement for vigilance writ large. If the laws drive our opponents to earth, and they choose to make their conspiracies in secret dens, it is my office which shall hound them out.

Extract from 'The Trial of Samuel Taylor Coleridge & William Wordsworth for High Treason at the Session House in the Old Bailey: published from Mr Gurney's Short-Hand Notes', Holborn, 1798. Price 7s.

The Court being opened and Samuel Taylor Coleridge & William Wordsworth set to the Bar, the Jurors returned by the Sheriff were called over:

Enos Thistlewood, Garlick Hill, Tallow-Chandler – Excused on Account of Age

Edward Read, Fenchurch Street, Upholsterer – Ill

William Darke, Bread Street, Merchant – Sworn

John Irvine, St Ann's Lane, Watchmaker – Challenged on the Part of the Crown

Harvey Mortimer, St Paul's Church-Yard, Gentleman – Sworn

Henry Thorne, Racquet Court, Dentist – Not a freeholder

Thomas Collier, Mincing Lane, Wine Merchant – Sworn

Edward Shirley, Fleet Street, Silversmith – Sworn

Thomas Brown – Excused being an Apothecary and Man Midwife

Henry Hayes, Grub Street, Soap-Boiler – Not a freeholder

Benjamin Coxwell, Rood Lane, Grocer – Sworn

Joseph Child, Lombard Street, Banker – Out of Town before Summons

John Handyside, Fleet Street, Druggist – Not a freeholder

Peter Berwick, Great St Helen's, Carpenter – Sworn

John Webb, Cheapside, Glover – His name not John but George

Duncan Pring, Little St Thomas Apostle, Skin Broker – Sworn

John Fothergill, Little Love Lane, Merchant   Sworn

Frederick Knight, Mark Lane, Corn Factor – Dead

Joseph Bannister, Fleet Street, Bookseller – One of the People called Quakers

Charles Shaw, Aldersgate Street, Distiller – Sworn

John Wayland, Cornhill, Sugar Banker – Sworn

William Brooks, High Timber St, Lighter Man – Excused on Account of Deafness

Nathaniel Coffin, Fore Street, Undertaker – Sworn

Samuel Mountfield, Aldgate High St, Inn-holder – Ill

George Gould, Gracechurch St, Gilder – Sworn

Memorandum from John King to the Duke of Portland, Tuesday 6ᵗʰ March 1798

I have received word from the Sessions House of the jury empanelled to hear the charge of High Treason.

Your Grace will be pleased to own an acquaintance with the names of sundry good men. But a further person on whom it was thought reliance could be placed was at the last moment disregarded since he was not a freeholder.

None the less, the only name on the list considered to be doubtful, a distiller, will assuredly find himself much alone if he again incline to those views expressed on a former occasion when, like the prisoners, he became too easily intoxicated with his own noxious productions.

Extract from the Notebooks of an Unidentified Student of Law, 1798

Trial of Samuel <u>Coleridge</u> & William <u>Wordsworth</u>.

Accused of High Treason.

(Forced to part with large sum to secure place in public gallery.)

Mr Gurney appeared for Defence. 5 years at bar. Son of Mr G. who sits before Bench scribbling down notes for Court Proceedings.

Mr Scott appeared for Prosecution.

Much curiosity in public gallery at appearance of prisoners. Mirror placed above bar, so that all might observe their expressions.

C possessed of large staring eyes.

W sallow & thin with scar on cheek.

Extract from 'The Trial ...', Holborn, 1798

The indictment having been read, the prosecution was opened by the Attorney General who, in a very eloquent and impartial manner, laid before the jury the whole of the charges.

Mr Attorney General: May it please your Lordship, Gentlemen of the Jury, I am called upon to address you with reference to a case of a most serious nature, whether it is considered with regard to the public, or with regard to the prisoners who stand at the bar.

The indictment you have heard read charges these prisoners with the highest offence known to the law of your country. It is a charge that should be most carefully examined. For there can be no more important question submitted to judicial determination than that of guilt or innocence upon a charge of High Treason.

If so base and atrocious crime is proved, it is your solemn duty, however painful the discharge of that duty may be, to convict the prisoners and deliver them up to that punishment which the law has so justly provided for their offence.

But if you are not satisfied that such a crime is proved, you shall do no more than your duty to acquit them. The prisoners' title to justice can never be forfeited in a court administering English law by an English jury under the direction of English judges.

I shall now proceed to state to you, with as much brevity as I can, the outline of the case as it respects the prisoners at the bar, and the evidence by which the charge will be proved:

Gentlemen, the essence of these men's treachery is conspiracy. Conspiracy to enter into a traitorous correspondence with the French; and to encourage, by means of a devious cipher, the quartering of enemy troops in this country at a large and secluded property rented for the purpose by Mr Wordsworth.

You will hear by witness testimony that, as soon as Mr Wordsworth secured the lease of this property, which is located close by the Bristol Channel, he and Mr Coleridge set about surveying the local country by day and night, recording their observations in a secret portfolio. You will also hear that the same activity was carried out near Fishguard by a person whose identity has never been established, only a few months prior to the landing of Colonel Tate and his Legion Noir.

Gentlemen, you will then learn what manner of man is Mr Wordsworth. You will hear how he has sought to publish a manuscript glorying in the abominable violence in France – in which he signs himself 'A Republican' – and how he has produced satires lampooning His Majesty. You will hear that he was formerly in that nation on several occasions, and that, during these visits, he attended meetings of the local Jacobin club, befriending a French army officer whose present whereabouts are unknown.

With regard to Mr Coleridge, you will hear that, upon the commencement of war, he contrived to obtain knowledge of the militia under an assumed name. He then had himself discharged insane and proceeded to Bristol, the very place whose destruction was the object of Colonel Tate's invasion force, where he propounded a series of lectures so inflammatory that public disorder was the outcome. You would do well to bear in mind that the subject of one of these lectures was *Literature – its revolutionary powers*.

From another witness, a man who proceeded to Somerset at the request of the Office of His Grace the Duke of Portland, you will hear that Mr Coleridge proclaimed Mr Wordsworth's aim to be nothing less than the overthrow of established law and government. You will also hear that Mr Coleridge himself soon after embarked upon a journey west along the coast, during which he had frequent resort to a spyglass to study vessels in the channel.

You will be shown a piece of paper which was surrendered from Mr Coleridge's possession during this journey. It will deserve your particular attention. For although the words upon it may appear to be nothing but mere nonsense rhyme, I assure you they are anything but nonsensical. On the contrary, this verse was skilfully enciphered so as to inform Monsieur Carnot of the Military Council in Paris, that the place of rendezvous for a French landing party would be Mr Wordsworth's property.

Gentlemen, you have before you a case of great importance. It is a case which I am sure you will listen to with great attention. And I am confident that you will decide it with unimpeachable integrity.

If I prove the facts as stated, and if you should find distinct evidence of the intention behind these actions, there can be no doubt that these men are guilty of High Treason.

Whatever your verdict, I know the country will feel a perfect satisfaction that it has had the case fairly, fully, and maturely deliberated by the twelve men to whom I have had the honour of addressing myself.

I shall now proceed to call the first witness.

Extract from 'The Trial ...', Holborn, 1798

Mr Christopher Trickie sworn
Examined by Mr Solicitor General

<u>Mr Solicitor General</u>: You inhabit a dwelling known as the Dog Pound?

<u>Trickie</u>: Yes.

<u>Mr Solicitor General</u>: And you lived there when Mr Wordsworth took up residence at Alfoxton House last July?

<u>Trickie</u>: Yes.

<u>Mr Solicitor General</u>: Did you ever see Mr Coleridge before that?

<u>Trickie</u>: No. The first time I saw him was when he came with Mr Wordsworth and another man to see the house.

<u>Mr Solicitor General</u>: They inspected the property?

<u>Trickie</u>: Yes. They said it suited all their purposes.

<u>Mr Solicitor General</u>: How do you know that?

<u>Trickie</u>: I live at the end of the drive. They spoke of it as they passed by.

<u>Mr Solicitor General</u>: The drive is long?

<u>Trickie</u>: About half a mile.

Mr Solicitor General: So the house is entirely removed from all other properties?

Trickie: It is.

Mr Solicitor General: What are its surroundings?

Trickie: Woods. Except to the sea. It has a view of the sea.

Mr Solicitor General: When did you next see Mr Coleridge?

Trickie: Not long after.

Mr Solicitor General: He visited the property?

Trickie: Yes.

Mr Solicitor General: He was a frequent visitor?

Trickie: Yes.

Mr Solicitor General: It is true to say that these men passed a great deal of time together?

Trickie: Yes. And not just by day neither.

Mr Solicitor General: What were they engaged in doing?

Trickie: They walked out on the hills. They carried a spyglass. They had pencils and a book. They set down what they saw in this book.

Mr Solicitor General: Did these observations take the form of charts and sketches?

Trickie: I do not know. They kept the book well hid.

Mr Solicitor General: But there was perhaps some particular object of their studies?

Trickie: The river near my house.

Mr Solicitor General: How do you know?

Trickie: They asked if it could be passed down to the sea.

Mr Solicitor General: They possessed a boat?

Trickie: No.

Mr Solicitor General: Then what was the reason for their inquiry?

Trickie: They did not say.

Mr Solicitor General: What did you tell them?

Trickie: I said it could not.

Mr Solicitor General: What was their response?

Trickie: They looked a long time at the river. They looked at it all the way down to the sea.

Mr Solicitor General: They did not explain this strange manner of proceeding?

Trickie: I heard them say they expected reward. Some other men came to Alfoxton soon after. I do not know why.

Cross-Examined by Mr Gurney

Mr Gurney: You plainly dwelt in close proximity to Mr Wordsworth?

Trickie: Yes.

Mr Gurney: But you had not many dealings with him?

Trickie: No.

Mr Gurney: Not as many as you would have liked, seeing as you are the keeper of hounds?

Trickie: Enough.

Mr Gurney: And I take it Mr Wordsworth did not employ a local servant?

Trickie: He was careful who went into the house.

Mr Gurney: So it is true to say that he did not spend as much money as some would have liked, at a time when the price of bread is no bargain?

Trickie: I cannot say.

Mr Gurney: But if Mr Wordsworth chose to be careful with his money, that is his business, is it not? That is the very liberty we seek to defend. It is no excuse for malicious gossip.

Trickie: I -

Mr Gurney: No matter. Perhaps you are familiar with the river of this city?

Trickie: I have seen it.

Mr Gurney: Then you will do me the honour of saying whether the Thames is bigger or smaller than the river near your dwelling?

Trickie: Bigger.

Mr Gurney: A lot bigger? Or a little bigger?

Trickie: A lot bigger.

Mr Gurney: In truth, the river near your house is little more than a brook, is it?

Trickie: No.

Mr Gurney: And there is no chance of a French frigate sailing up it?

Mr Attorney General: These men may have wished to use it to move supplies.

Mr Gurney: I do declare that the only ship which could have navigated such a stream must have been launched in a puddle. Now, Mr Trickie, you said these men did not show you the book in which they recorded their observations?

Trickie: No.

Mr Gurney: But why should they? No member of the Jury would volunteer the contents of his private memorandum book to a neighbour he scarcely knew.

Trickie: I only said they kept it well hid.

Mr Gurney: But that is no different to what any man would have done. Now, you also say you saw these men out by night?

Trickie: Yes.

Mr Gurney: What, pray, enticed you out on the coast after dark?

Trickie: I heard my dogs bark.

Mr Gurney: Indeed. But you are certain, although it was dark and you are blind in one eye, that it was these men you saw?

Trickie: There was a moon. And I was not the only man to do so.

Mr Gurney: I am not certain if that answers my question, but I thank you, sir. Gentlemen of the Jury, if there is any man present who has made secret observations to be rid of another he did not like, I would contend that we are closer to being able to identify that man.

Extract from 'The Trial …', Holborn, 1798

<u>Mr Attorney General</u>: Gentlemen of the Jury, it is my intention to read to you certain passages from a manuscript discovered among Mr Wordsworth's papers. It is written in his own hand, he sought to publish it, and, as you may see from the evidence of your own eyes, he signed it A REPUBLICAN:

"Under every government of modern times, till the foundation of the American Republic, the bulk of mankind have appeared incapable of discerning their true interests."

"In France royalty is no more. The person of the last anointed is no more also; and I flatter myself I am not alone, even in this kingdom, when I wish that it may please the Almighty neither by the hands of His priests nor His nobles to raise his posterity to the rank of his ancestors."

"The office of king is a trial to which human virtue is not equal. Pure and universal representation, by which alone liberty can be secured, cannot, I think, exist together with monarchy."

Extract from the Notebooks of an Unidentified Student of Law, 1798

C directed ireful gaze at irons kept to hold convicts while they are branded. Twice had to be restrained from starting up to remonstrate.

W impassive, even when it was suggested he is regicide.

Extract from 'The Trial …', Holborn, 1798

Mr George Heaton sworn
Examined by Mr Solicitor General

<u>Mr Solicitor General</u>: How came you to be in the area close by Alfoxton House?

<u>Mr Heaton</u>: I went there at the request of the Office of His Grace the Duke of Portland.

<u>Mr Solicitor General</u>: To what purpose?

<u>Mr Heaton</u>: To look into the nature of the place. And to see if these men were engaged in a plot to encourage a French invasion.

<u>Mr Solicitor General</u>: What did you discover upon your arrival?

<u>Mr Heaton</u>: I saw that Alfoxton House is a fine place for a military camp. It is secluded from the local people. There is shelter for many troops, a plentiful supply of fresh water, and there is venison in abundance. The nearest militia is quartered many miles away.

<u>Mr Solicitor General</u>: What did you observe of the prisoners?

<u>Mr Heaton</u>: I saw that they were taken up with some pressing concern. Mr Coleridge kept a light burning late into the night. And he inhabited a house at the farthest edge of Nether Stowey, that he might steal away to visit his compatriot.

Mr Solicitor General: Did you find out what it was that so consumed their energies?

Mr Heaton: I overheard a conversation between Mr Wordsworth's sister and Mr Coleridge as they walked secretly in the woods. Mr Coleridge said that Mr Wordsworth was engaged in a work of great benefit to mankind. All he required for his purpose was the absence of established law and government. Mr Wordsworth's sister added that there was great potential in Mr Coleridge's work concerning the local river.

Mr Solicitor General: The two of them consorted in these woods, although Mr Coleridge is a married man?

Mr Heaton: They did.

Mr Solicitor General: And what happened when Mr Coleridge next visited Alfoxton House?

Mr Heaton: I saw him to obtain a particular book from Mr Wordsworth.

Mr Solicitor General: What was this book?

Mr Heaton: It was an old book. A description of some travels by a man named Purchas.

Mr Solicitor General: Mark that, Gentlemen, it is important. What did he do next?

Mr Heaton: The next day, he set out on a journey west along the coast. I saw him making frequent observations of the ships in the Bristol Channel.

Mr Solicitor General: He searched for one vessel in particular?

Mr Heaton: It seemed so to me.

Mr Solicitor General: He intended an assignation?

Mr Heaton: He later lingered at a deserted church as if he awaited someone. Then he was seized by illness and forced to seek shelter at a farm.

Mr Solicitor General: What was the name of this farm?

Mr Heaton: Withycombe Farm.

Mr Solicitor General: You followed him there?

Mr Heaton: I did.

Mr Solicitor General: What did you see?

Mr Heaton: I saw him scribble down some words in great haste, as if he feared he might forget them in his malady.

Mr Solicitor General: They are the words you see before you on this paper?

Mr Heaton: Yes.

Mr Solicitor General: You are certain?

Mr Heaton: Yes.

Mr Solicitor General: But Mr Coleridge evidently recovered from his indisposition?

Mr Heaton: He did. But he abandoned his journey and returned home in a great depression of spirits.

Mr Solicitor General: For how long did this fit of melancholy persist?

Mr Heaton: For some weeks. It was about the time that news arrived of Admiral Duncan's great victory at Camperdown.

Mr Solicitor General: And this brought a conclusion to these men's strange activities?

Mr Heaton: It did for a while. But then I heard them devising plans to reach the continent by way of Hamburg.

Mr Solicitor General: To what purpose?

Mr Heaton: I do not know. But I heard they contemplated a dark crime which would encompass a ship.

Cross-Examined by Mr Gurney

Mr Gurney: When Mr Coleridge made his journey west, did you see him signal to any vessel in the channel?

Mr Heaton: I am not sure.

Mr Gurney: Why not?

Mr Heaton: He may have used a secret signal.

Mr Gurney: But he made no obvious signal?

Mr Heaton: No.

Mr Gurney: And he met with no person, nor handed any document to any person, before he was obliged to seek shelter at Withycombe Farm?

Mr Heaton: He spoke with the landlord of the Bell at Watchet. And with several tradesmen in Porlock.

Mr Gurney: But you do not suspect these persons to be enemy spies as well?

Mr Heaton: No.

Mr Gurney: Then you would concur that, during his journey west along the coast, Mr Coleridge behaved in a manner entirely consistent with his declared method of poetic composition?

Mr Heaton: It is a strange part of the country to make poems in, when we are under constant threat of invasion.

Mr Gurney: Forgive me, Mr Heaton, but I do not think that the government has yet taken it upon itself to specify those regions of the country in which it is permitted to compose poetry. Now, did you see Mr Wordsworth reading this book by Purchas?

Mr Heaton: No.

Mr Gurney: And, from what you say, you are far from sure he possessed any knowledge of the nonsense rhyme which is flourished in court as evidence against both these men?

Mr Heaton: I cannot be certain.

Mr Gurney: Then I cannot be certain what may be deduced about the extent of these men's collaboration. How long have you been in the employ of the government?

Mr Heaton: Five years.

Mr Gurney: Five years of eavesdropping and spying on your fellow countrymen? Five years of infringing the very liberties we hold most dear?

Mr Heaton: I do this for my country.

Mr Gurney: You would not have us believe you do it entirely out of patriotism?

Mr Heaton: I do not comprehend you.

Mr Gurney: You receive financial reward, do you not?

Mr Heaton: I must have payment for victual. But it is better to earn a crust by serving my country than by betraying it.

Mr Gurney: Well said. But it is equally certain that, if you set foot in Somerset at the request of His Grace the Duke of Portland and obtained monies from his office for spying on these men, you are no disinterested witness.

Extract from 'The Trial ...', Holborn, 1798

<u>Mr Attorney General</u>: Gentlemen, it is late in the day. But I must crave your indulgence in a matter of the gravest importance and the utmost delicacy.

I am at liberty to reveal that, in this time of war, there exists a department of men whose duty is to break those codes employed by our enemies to conceal their malign intentions. By necessity, these men occupy a situation of the greatest obscurity. It is beyond the bounds of possibility I might summon one of them to give evidence before this court.

I must, therefore, content myself with reading out a statement by one of them – let us call him Mr Maddison – concerning the verse borne west along the coast by Mr Coleridge. The verity of his comments you will observe by perusing the evidence before you; both the verse itself and the passage from the travel book by Purchas, which, as you will recall, was the very book extracted by Mr Coleridge from the library at Alfoxton House.

Mr Maddison's statement read aloud

"I, Maddison, conceive this verse to be a form of coded communication.

"The curious alterations made between the verse and the travel book serve to encipher a secret meaning. The river is given the name Alph, when it has none in the book. And the measurement of land is altered from sixteen miles to "twice five", or ten. When placed together, these changes spell out ALPH'TEN, which is a sure abbreviation of Mr Wordsworth's residence.

"Of equal curiosity, the rhyme ends with the word WAR, although this bears no relation to what has gone before. I conceive this to be a signal to the enemy to commence preparations for the landing of troops.

"The intended recipient of this message was Monsieur Carnot, the Organiser of Victory in Paris. You will note that his identity is contained within the ingenious combination of Khan and water, which, when the latter is rendered into French, together reveal his name: KHAN-EAU.

Mr Attorney General: Gentlemen, it is you who must decide whether, by coincidence alone, this verse makes allusion to Alfoxton House and Monsieur Carnot. It is you who must account for the placing of the word WAR at the end of the verse, even though it bears no relation to what goes before.

As you do so, I would invite you to ponder whether the appearance of nonsense verse is not an essential part of the deception. And to ask yourselves again if it is likely, in view of the grievances these men have long entertained, that they would remove themselves to an area of interest to this nation's enemy, and there devote their energies to the composition of nonsense rhyme.

The Court adjourned from half past ten till eight o'clock on Wednesday morning.

Extract from the Journal of the Duke of Portland, Tuesday 6th March 1798

The day is ours.

Our witnesses stood firm – all save the yokel – and we produce evidence which cannot be easily gainsaid. I am assured Mr Gurney inflicted no serious damage.

A verdict is expected before tomorrow is out; to be followed, no doubt, by an application for pardon. Our resolve must be adamantine. The end of justice is public example. The improper exercise of mercy would be cruelty in the extreme.

This judgment must remind people of their duty of vigilance. The advent of Spring is almost upon us. Bonaparte will not much longer be content at playing cards with Thomas Paine.

Extract from 'The Trial ...', Holborn, 1798

On Wednesday morning the trial proceeded as follows

<u>Mr Gurney</u>: May it please your Lordship, Gentlemen of the Jury, we are come to that stage of the trial in which I am to address you on the part of the prisoners.

I believe it was my Lord Chief Justice Coke who first set down of the statute of treason that it must be decided *"upon direct and manifest proof, not upon conjectural presumptions or inferences, or strains of wit, but upon good and sufficient proof."*

I read you these words, for I depend on it you will take into account the established principle that the greater the crime imputed to the prisoners, the greater the degree of caution which must be exercised before delivering them over to that vengeance which necessarily awaits.

I am persuaded that you will arrive at your verdict impartially, and with that integrity which is your true portion of proper virtue. I am confident that honest, just, and humane men as you are, you will not touch a hair of these men's heads, unless you are perfectly convinced that you have seen clear, distinct, and manifest evidence which amounts to an open act of treason.

I now bring you to the particular evidence in the case.

Extract from the Notebooks of an Unidentified Student of Law

Counsel for Defence addressed Jury with vigour & eloquence.

Asked if it were likely enemy plans depended on rhyme carried to Military Council in Paris? Or on despatch of troops to obscure residence let by clergyman's relict?

Reminded all present that French desired to set each man against his neighbour.

- Re. <u>Fishguard</u>: no proof that these observations anticipated landing of Col Tate.

- Re. <u>Manuscript Signed 'A Republican'</u>: this was composed when W barely a man. He & his orphaned siblings had been cruelly abused by Earl of Lowther, who made beggars of them rather than pay what was rightly theirs. Such iniquity prompted a spontaneous overflow of feeling against aristocracy which W now regretted.

- Re. <u>C's lectures in Bristol</u>: one speech upon the revolutionary power of literature did not prove intent to raise insurrection, whether by verse, drama, or epistolary novel.

- Re. <u>Christopher Trickie</u>: his evidence nothing but a false construal of literary endeavour, encouraged by the prevailing invasion madness.

- Re. <u>George Heaton</u>: as above, but more so, since Heaton in employ of government.

- Re. <u>W's sister</u>: whatever she said must be disregarded, for she was now confined insane.

- Re. <u>Nonsense Rhyme Carried West by Coleridge</u>: W not with C at time & knew nothing of it.

- Re. <u>Nonsense Rhyme Carried West by Coleridge</u>: each change cited as evidence of cipher actually made for poetic effect. Alph the sacred muse of poetry; "twice five" nicer than sixteen. Might as well suggest "Woman Wailing" stood for WW, or that, since Khan's residence a dome, C desired to storm St Paul's Cathedral.

- Re. <u>Nonsense Rhyme Carried West by Coleridge</u>: 'war' not last word. Poem stolen before it could be finished. Only possible adverse verdict against C as poet.

Extract from 'The Trial ...', Holborn, 1798

Mr Gurney: These witnesses are to character. I believe it will not be exceptionable to call them all in together.

The Attorney General consented.

Charles Lamb sworn. Examined by Mr Gurney

Mr Lamb: I am a clerk in the East India office. I have known Mr Coleridge since we were at school at Christ's Hospital.

Mr Gurney: Is he a humane good-natured man?

Mr Lamb: I have always thought so. I never saw anything amiss of him.

Basil Montagu sworn

Mr Montagu: I have known Mr Wordsworth four years. I consider the occasion of meeting him to be one of the most fortunate of my life.

Mr Gurney: Have you known him well?

Mr Montagu: Rather so. He is a quiet, easy, good-natured man. So much so, that I entrusted him with the upbringing of my son whose dear mother perished at his birth.

Mr Gurney: Mr Wordsworth fulfilled this duty to your satisfaction?

Mr Montagu: Most certainly. The boy is a contented child and knows his letters well.

Joseph Cottle sworn

<u>Mr Cottle</u>: I am a bookseller of Corn Street, Bristol. I have known these men three years. I visited them in Nether Stowey last summer.

<u>Mr Gurney</u>: What is their character?

<u>Mr Cottle</u>: I have always looked on them as exceedingly good, humane men. I never thought either of them would commit the least crime.

Extract from 'The Trial …', Holborn, 1798

<u>Mr Gurney:</u> Gentlemen of the Jury, I cannot fail to have perceived from the nature of the evidence that certain prejudices may have arisen in your minds with regard to the prisoners at the bar. But there is no proof which ought to satisfy your minds in a case of life and death.

I entreat you to reach a verdict which will send these men forth among their fellow subjects with honour and not condemn them to an ignominious death. For, if there are persons in this country who fancy we have not attained that degree of perfect freedom which is capable of being attained, nothing will so completely satisfy them of their mistake as a verdict of Not Guilty.

I have little more to add, other than to return to you my most sincere and grateful thanks for the profound attention you have been pleased to pay me during my address.

Extract from the Notebooks of an Unidentified Student of Law

Lord Chief Justice reminded Jury he had power to interrogate them as to verdict & to demand they reconsider if cause to do so.

They must rely on evidence presented. Must be certain these men had not mended their ways, but had advanced beyond redemption & acted with traitorous intent.

No further guidance. Except to look into own hearts & determine if country as safe against French with prisoners at large as if they were not so.

Memorandum received at the Home Office,
Wednesday 7th March 1798

MAKE READY FOR A VERDICT

The Justice has summed up & the Jury is gone into a huddle. They may yet withdraw to another room for lengthier deliberation. But this contains no lighted fire & they are to receive no nourishment until a decision is reached.

Extract from the Notebooks of an Unidentified Student of Law

Jury requested to depart court.

(Uproar in gallery. One man shouted out they were infiltrated by d----d Jacobins who meant to hold out until others agreed to recommend mercy. Another called this arrant falsehood & declared Trickie to be a deceiving bumpkin.)

Decision taken to clear court.

**Memorandum Received at the Home Office,
Wednesday 7ᵗʰ March 1798**

The Jury has requested to pursue its deliberations beyond the courtroom.

Mr Scott says this should not be taken ill, but is rather a consequence of the severity of the crime imputed to the prisoners. A HIGH DEGREE OF CAUTION IS MOST OFTEN SEEN TO BE EXERCISED BEFORE A VERDICT OF GUILTY IS RETURNED.

**Memorandum Received at the Home Office,
Wednesday 7ᵗʰ March 1798**

COLERIDGE IS FOUND GUILTY; WORDSWORTH IS
CONVICTED ALSO, BUT WITH A RECOMMENDATION
TO MERCY.

The foreman of the Jury has been interrogated & says that,
since the code is in C's hand & he proceeded west alone,
there is dispute as to W's complicity. It is thought possible
by some that C's fervid character may have seduced W
into acts of which he but half knew the consequence.

In short, this is the only verdict upon which they can
agree.

Extract from the Journal of the Duke of Portland, Wednesday 7ᵗʰ March 1798

As soon as these tidings were received, I attended Mr Pitt who appeared ghastly pale, but made light of this. He declared himself pleased to know there would be no repetition of those shameful scenes of '94, when the traitors were drawn in triumph through the streets by an ignorant multitude. The Attorney General had surpassed himself & must prove a worthy successor to Sir J. Eyre as Lord Chief Justice of the Common Pleas.

I told him that, with each passing day, I saw new evidence of the threat posed by our enemies within these shores. I considered it desirable His Majesty's review of these men's sentences be carried out with all expedition. I hoped I was not precipitate in drawing up plans for the deployment of horse guards – and a patrol of men from Bow Street and other Peace Offices – upon the day of these men's execution.

Mr Pitt seemed in no mood for disputation.

I therefore took the opportunity to urge a rapid expansion of this nation's domestic security arrangements. And I was pleased to recommend the appointment of Mr John King as a Superintendent of the Alien Office for the next five years.

Extract from 'The Trial ...', Holborn, 1798

Lord Chief Justice Eyre: Samuel Taylor Coleridge and William Wordsworth, you have, after a long and, I trust, impartial trial, been severally convicted by a most respectable jury of the High Treason which is by your indictment charged upon you.

In this, your abominable conspiracy, you have schemed to abet the enemies of this nation in the overthrow of that constitution which, in its established freedoms and boasted usages, has long maintained among us that just and rational equality of right; and which has, for many ages, been the envy and admiration of the world.

It is to be hoped that, by the calamitous consequences which attend your crime, you will afford a melancholy but instructive example to your fellow subjects. May they learn properly to value the humble but secure blessings of an industrious and quiet life – of an honest and loyal course of conduct – and by so doing increase the stock of public happiness and security.

The only thing that remains for me is the sad and painful task of pronouncing against you the awful sentence which the law denounces against your crime. May you both, during the period of your remaining lives, see fit to seek that salvation which, from the infinite mercy of God, is yet attainable by effectual penitence and prevailing prayer.

The sentence is, and this court doth adjudge, that you Samuel Taylor Coleridge and you William Wordsworth, be taken from the place whence you came and drawn on hurdles to the place of execution. There you are to be hanged by the neck, but not until you are dead; then your bodies taken down, your bowels torn out and burned before your faces, your heads cut off, and your bodies divided into four quarters; your heads and quarters then to be at the disposal of the King.

May Almighty God have mercy upon your souls.

Petition Addressed to His Majesty King George III by William Cookson, Canon of Windsor and former Tutor to Their Royal Highnesses, the Young Princes, Friday 9th March 1798

I do most humbly and reverently beseech Your Majesty to grant my nephew, William Wordsworth, that mercy which is the great ornament and bright luminary of Your Majesty's most revered Person.

I entreat Your Majesty to consider the ordeal of suffering already borne by his loyal and patriotic family, who have ever exerted themselves in the service of Your Majesty. With what hideous effect must their disgrace be multiplied by his public execution.

I beg Your Majesty to spare the life of my nephew, that he might strive, through manifold acts of penitence, to earn that redemption which must ever be his signal object, all the remaining days of his existence.

**Extract from the Journal of the Duke of Portland,
Monday 12ᵗʰ March 1798**

Rumours of French gunboats sighted off the coast of
Dover. Some do not wait for corroboration, but urge their
carriages from the capital with despatch.

Plans are drawn up for a hasty movement of cavalry
and troops about the country. Those nearest to London
shall deploy as needed. The militia is readied all along
the coast. Word is sent to Ireland to expect an attack by
Napper Tandy, who has been given command of a corvette
and means to make for that place to raise rebellion. (May
he be consigned to the depths.)

I thank Divine Providence we effected the apprehension
of the traitorous priest before he succeeded in obtaining
illicit passage from the coast of Kent.

Record of a Conversation between the Prime Minister & the Home Secretary, Tuesday 13th March 1798

The PRIME MINISTER stated that, upon a review of Wordsworth's sentence, he was disposed to favour the recommendation of the Jury that justice should be tempered with mercy.

The HOME SECRETARY declared himself aghast. Even if the latest invasion scare had come to nothing, this was no time for leniency. The great object of punishment was to serve as a deterrent.

The PRIME MINISTER noted that Wordsworth would be transported in irons to Botany Bay; a place from which more than one self-declared "patriot" had never returned.

The HOME SECRETARY answered that if the Government sanctioned his pardon, it must undermine the entire rule of law. Was it not set down on the highest authority that a traitor ought to be exterminated as a bane to human society? These men had intended no mercy and deserved none in return.

The PRIME MINISTER observed that the prerogative of mercy was governed by no fixed rules of procedure. The contrast with France, where justice was summary and government by decree, could not be more pertinent. No opponent would again accuse the Government of exercising the terror it claimed to abhor when it had so evidently respected the wishes of a Jury of free-born

Englishmen. Besides, was not Coleridge indubitably the more dangerous man?

The HOME SECRETARY replied that Wordsworth had penned a regicide tract. It was inconceivable His Majesty might be persuaded to grant such a villain mercy.

The PRIME MINISTER declared that the pardon was countenanced at His Majesty's suggestion.

The HOME SECRETARY did not immediately reply.

The PRIME MINISTER said he hoped this question might be resolved soon, for there were other important matters to discuss. In particular, he desired to confirm the establishment of the Alien Office on a permanent footing, and to discuss what portion of the extra monies soon to be made available to the Home Office would be allocated to it; such that Mr King, in his new situation, might best continue his excellent service to the nation.

The HOME SECRETARY said that it had only ever been his concern that men ought to obtain what they deserved.

The PRIME MINISTER replied he had always sought to govern by such principles. He hoped this natural coincidence of mind would prove the foundation for many more years of collaboration at this most dangerous of times.

The HOME SECRETARY admitted there may well be advantage to a commutation of Wordsworth's sentence, so long as Coleridge's fate remained exemplary.

The PRIME MINISTER undertook to inform His Majesty of this resolution.

Extract from 'The Observer', Sunday 18th March 1798

As to the other man, a warrant for his execution is made out and delivered to the Tower. A scaffold will be erected there, it being inadvisable at this time for a person convicted of such a crime to be drawn through the streets.

We further understand that the cutting out of the heart of the malefactor, quartering, etc, is very humanely and properly to be dispensed with, His Majesty having graciously remitted that part of the sentence.

There is some speculation that the condemned man may yet obtain a reprieve. We do not consider this likely. The act of remitment is rather to be taken as a sign that the magistrates now have in their possession a full confession of his ignoble treachery.

Extract from the Journal of the Duke of Portland, Sunday 18th March 1798

I told Mr Pitt that no matter what appeared in the newspaper, Newgate must be the place of execution. A large crowd of people wished to attend who loathed this crime. It would not be proper to deny them the admonitory spectacle of justice.

Mr Pitt said it was precisely the assembly of thousands which he feared. London contained a mass of depredators, ever ready to take advantage in the hour of public danger. This might turn out the occasion of insurrection and a storming of the city gaols. The Tower was a place altogether more easily defended.

I replied that, if we did not set up the scaffold in a place accessible to such a crowd, this itself would be the occasion of disorder. Besides, was not the Tower reserved for the execution of the nobility? A man such as Coleridge could never be accorded this privilege. He must be drawn through the streets to Newgate.

There ensued an unaccountable discussion in which each man present endeavoured to persuade the other of his opinion, but, as he did so, only persuaded himself to the contrary. In the end, Mr Pitt removed a coin from his pocket.

I called for heads & won.

Memorandum from John King to the Duke of Portland, Tuesday 20th March 1798

I write to inform Your Grace that a Minister of Religion has attended Coleridge in his cell with as much tenderness and humanity as the awful nature of the case requires. He did not omit to remind the condemned man of the power of effectual penitence. He has left with him a copy of 'Evidences of Christianity'.

However, I do not think it likely that Coleridge shall willingly confess his crime, even upon the very scaffold.

Extract from 'The Newgate Calendar'

At four o'clock the next morning, the 21st of March, the drum beat at the Horse Guards as a signal for the cavalry to assemble. Two hours later, the Life Guards arrived and took up their stations. All the Bow Street patrol had been on duty all day and night. The military near London were drawn up close to the city.

At half-past six, the prison bell rang and the prisoner was brought down. His irons were knocked off and his arms bound with rope. He was placed on a hurdle and drawn to the place of execution, preceded by the Sheriff and a Minister of Religion.

A coffin was brought up. It was placed on the platform on which the drop had been erected. Two bags of sawdust were placed beside it, to catch the blood when the head was severed from the body. There were about a hundred spectators on the platform, some of whom were persons of distinction.

At six minutes before nine o'clock, the signal was given, the platform dropped, and the prisoner was launched into eternity. After hanging about half-an-hour till he was quite dead, his body was cut down and his head placed upon the block. After his coat was taken off, his head was severed from his body by persons engaged on purpose to perform that ceremony.

The executioner took the head by the hair and carried it to the edge of the parapet. He held it up to the view of the populace, exclaiming: "This is the head of a traitor, Samuel Taylor Coleridge". The same ceremony was performed at the other side.

The mortal remains of this man were conveyed into the prison. They were covered in quicklime and interred in unhallowed ground.

Extract from a Report sent by the Lord Mayor of London to the Home Secretary, Wednesday 21st March 1798

By far the most dissatisfaction was expressed at the decapitation. Yet it was but momentary. On the whole, there has seldom been a more tranquil execution witnessed. The troops were so dispersed that, whichever way the populace approached the Old Bailey, they must be seen to deter any attempt at rescue.

The mob are beginning slowly to disperse. Unless anything fresh were to occur, I think it will be unnecessary to trouble Your Grace with any further account of this unpleasant business.

Memorandum from John King to the Duke of Portland, Friday 22nd June 1798

I write to inform Your Grace that the vessel which is to bear William Wordsworth and several accomplices of the late Father O'Coigly to Botany Bay will depart these shores three weeks' hence on the 13th July.

Copy of John King's Letter to George Heaton, Saturday 30th June 1798

Sir

The time is come for you to depart these shores upon the business we have formerly discussed, in the company of the bearer of this letter.

When you reach land, you are to employ your newfound acquaintance with the Portuguese tongue to obtain information as to the whereabouts of Mr Southey. When he is discovered, observe him like a hawk. Does he write or make sketches? Is he visited by strange men of an Hibernian extraction? What is his interest in the movement of shipping at the entrance to the Mediterranean?

You are to conduct yourself with the greatest of caution. Do not presume that Mrs Coleridge has not sentience to penetrate your true identity. These people will not again be found wanting in resolution to repel your attentions.

You could expect no mercy at their hands.

– THE END –

Author's Note

The inspiration for this novel comes from a well-documented incident: the despatch of a government spy to investigate the activities of Samuel Taylor Coleridge and William Wordsworth at a time of heightened invasion alarm.

Events swiftly deviate from recorded history. But it is salutary to think that, had a more paranoid state decided to delve a little deeper, the names of Coleridge and Wordsworth might have occupied a very different place in the annals of British history.

In constructing this alternative scenario, I have endeavoured to remain true to my sources. All quotations from the *Gentleman's Magazine* are genuine. So are those heading up Parts I and II, as well as the quotations from Wordsworth's unpublished seditious letter which he signed 'A Republican'. The two stanzas extracted from his poem 'The Convict' were first published in December 1797. All measures contemplated by Pitt and Portland for defending the coast are based on contemporary documentation. So is the government's preparation for, and conduct of, a treason trial.

The Battle of Camperdown took place on 11th October 1797. Father James O'Coigley (aka Captain Jones, aka

James Fevey) was one of five men arrested on the Kent coast in February 1798. He was executed for High Treason three months later.

Those readers puzzled to see *The Observer*, Britain's first Sunday newspaper, espousing the line of Pitt's government should note that, while it was founded in 1791 in a "spirit of enlightened Freedom, decent Toleration, and universal Benevolence", it had soon racked up such debts that it had little choice but to approach the government for a subsidy. This was granted in return for influence over editorial content.

It is impossible to date the composition of Coleridge's *Kubla Khan* with certainty. But there is good reason to date the lines seized by George Heaton in this novel to October 1797 (see Rosemary Ashton's work in the *Select Bibliography*). Coleridge himself claimed that the poem was drafted after taking opium to check an attack of dysentery. He also infamously claimed that it remained unfinished owing to the intervention of a person from Porlock.

We know that the excursion undertaken by Coleridge, Wordsworth and Dorothy, during which they developed ideas for *The Rime of the Ancient Mariner*, took place in November 1797. And we know that, a few weeks later, William and his sister set out for London with the aspiration of staging his verse drama, *The Borderers*, whose characters include Wallace, Lennox and Lacy.

Finally, it should be noted that the envisaged expedition to Germany did indeed take place. However Coleridge decided to leave behind his wife and two young sons. Tragically, the younger of these, Berkeley, died within six months. Coleridge's decision to linger in Germany some months after he received news of this bereavement inflicted irreparable damage on his marriage.

I summarise below the actual fate of many of the historical figures who feature in this novel. Readers desiring to know more of this fascinating period of history, or the brief but remarkable collaboration between the two poets, are recommended to the *Select Bibliography*.

- **William Henry Cavendish Bentinck, 3rd Duke of Portland (1738-1809)** was appointed Home Secretary in 1794 upon the formation of a war coalition. He eschewed crass populism and had a reputation as a shrewd and tough negotiator. He remained in office until 1801, later serving as Prime Minister from 1807 until his death. His own government was marred by his deteriorating health and by in-fighting among his ministers, two of whom went on to fight a scandalous duel.

- **Edmund Burke (1729-1797)** entered Parliament in 1765. He supported the emancipation of the American colonies, but his *Reflections on the Revolution in France* (1790) adopted a different line, correctly prophesying France's descent into violence and terror. To the horror of his erstwhile political allies, Burke became a vehement advocate of war against the Jacobins.

One of his last published works, *Letters on a Regicide Peace*, vigorously opposed any attempt by the British government to enter into peace negotiations. He died in July 1797.

- **Lazare Carnot (1753-1823)** was a distinguished military strategist and engineer who, as a member of the French National Convention, had voted in favour of the execution of Louis XVI. As a Minister of War, he played a crucial part in the success of the French army and was hailed as the 'Organiser of Victory'. He was ousted from power in the coup of September 1797. When Napoleon went on to proclaim himself Emperor, Carnot resigned from public life altogether and went into voluntary exile.

- **Samuel Taylor Coleridge (1772-1834)** lived a colourful existence after leaving Cambridge, at one point joining the army under a false name. Following a number of wild and impractical ventures, he gravitated toward radical politics. In Bristol, in 1795, he gave a series of lectures which provoked public disorder. After the passage of further repressive legislation and the failure of his radical journal *The Watchman* – and with a wife and child to support – he vowed to retire to the countryside. Upon his belated return from Germany in 1799, he was plagued by marital problems and an increasing addiction to opium. He formally separated from his wife in 1808 and passed the last eighteen years of his life at the home of the London physician, James Gillman. Much of the poetry for which he is remembered was composed during his time in Somerset. He also later published several influential works of philosophy, among them *Biographia Literaria* (1817). In this, he comically recounted the time when he was investigated by a government spy. It was only when EJ Eagleston published ground-breaking research based on the Home Office archives in 1934 that it became clear how narrowly the two poets had evaded serious danger.

- **John King (1759-1830)** attended Christ Church, Oxford, like the Duke of Portland before him. He married a daughter of the Bishop of Bath & Wells and enjoyed the patronage of Burke. He was promoted to Joint Superintendent of the Alien Office in 1798, later becoming Comptroller of Army Accounts having briefly served as an MP. He remained in public office all his days.

- **Thomas Paine (1737-1809)** published the *Rights of Man* as a response to Burke's *Reflections on the Revolution in France*. It was greeted with fervour by reformers and radicals, but the British government took a less enthusiastic view: Paine was forced to flee to France to avoid arrest. In 1797 he published a number of pamphlets advocating the invasion of Britain and was still lobbying for this as late as 1804. However, he was ostracised by Napoleon and later returned to the United States at the invitation of President Jefferson. After his death, his bones were exhumed by the English radical, William Cobbett, who bore them to Britain in the hope of interring them in their native soil. Permission was refused and Paine's bones were listed among Cobbett's personal effects when he died in 1835. Their present-day whereabouts remain a mystery.

- **William Pitt the Younger (1759-1806)** became Prime Minister in 1783, a position in which he worked (and drank) himself toward an early grave. Highly intelligent, erudite, and able, he led the government until 1801 and again from 1804 until his death. He is buried in Westminster Abbey.

- **Thomas Poole (1766-1837)** was apprenticed to his father's tannery and volunteered to attend a national delegation of tanners in London in 1791 which elected him to speak to Pitt concerning the distressed state of the industry. This sparked Poole's radical sympathies and helped inspire a deep attachment to Coleridge when the latter first visited Nether Stowey. In later years, the two men corresponded intermittently, but their final meeting took place in London just a few weeks before Coleridge's death. Poole continued to exhibit a benevolent interest in the welfare of local people all his life and established Nether Stowey's elementary school in 1812. He never married.

- **Sir John Scott (1751-1838)** was promoted to Chief Justice of the Common Pleas in 1799 and served as Lord Chancellor with only a brief interruption from 1801-27. He was succeeded as Attorney General by **Sir John Mitford (1748-1830)**, who appears in this novel as Solicitor General.

- **Richard Brinsley Sheridan (1751-1816)** is most famous for his plays *The Rivals* and *The School for Scandal*. With the proceeds of these, he purchased London's Drury Lane Theatre before entering Parliament in 1780. He was a frequent opponent of Pitt's government. When he failed to win re-election in 1812, his creditors closed in and he died in poverty having turned down an offer from the United States to settle his debts in acknowledgement of his political record.

- **Robert Southey (1774-1843)** was appointed Poet Laureate in 1813. He was a renowned biographer and scholar of Portuguese. He had visited Portugal, where his uncle owned a house near the Atlantic coast, in 1795-6. He was contemplating emigration two years later, so it is not far-fetched to place him there at this time. Despite quarrelling with Coleridge on several occasions, Southey dutifully supported Coleridge's family for many years (Coleridge's wife was Southey's sister-in-law). He was less supportive of a youthful Charlotte Bronte, whom he gravely informed "literature cannot be the business of a woman's life". No doubt he meant well.

- **Colonel William Tate** (dates unknown) was commander of the *Legion Noir*, a French force of more than 1,000 men which landed in South Wales in February 1797. This caused a financial panic which brought Britain to the brink of bankruptcy. The force was quickly overpowered, but Tate's orders were found to contain, among other objectives, the "destruction of Bristol ... the second city in England for riches and commerce" whose total ruin could not fail "to strike terror and amazement into the heart of the capital". This caused great shock, not least at the Home Office where a *Memorandum of the Coasts and Bays of Great Britain and Ireland and their General Defence* published just one month earlier had confidently asserted "the coasts of the Bristol Channel ... demand such peculiar and great arrangements to attack them, that they probably do not enter into the contemplation of an enemy." An American citizen, Tate was discharged on parole in November 1798. He was permitted to return to France where he allegedly ran up substantial debts "living with a lady friend of extravagant habits". In 1809 he returned to the United States. His subsequent fate is not known.

- **Dorothy Wordsworth (1771-1855)** remained devoted to her brother. Her journals and travel-writing, published posthumously, reveal she possessed no small talent in her own right. However she eschewed attention and chose to live out the life of a famous writer vicariously. It should perhaps be recalled that, at this time, few women found ways of making their voice heard in the public arena. It is no coincidence that the only woman who obtains a 'voice of her own' in this narrative is a propertied widow.

- **William Wordsworth (1770-1850)** was a stubborn and rebellious young man who, having attended St. John's College, Cambridge, turned down a career in the church planned for him by his uncle and made for France where he fathered an illegitimate daughter by his lover, Annette Vallon. Forced to return home by the war, he moved in radical circles and produced a ream of seditious material which sufficiently alarmed his elder brother, Richard, to precipitate an urgent warning to desist. After receiving a legacy from one of his friends, Wordsworth devoted himself to poetry and took up residence with his beloved sister. The two of them lived an isolated existence in Dorset until they were encouraged to move to Somerset by Coleridge, who harboured ambitions to collaborate with Wordsworth. This period culminated in one of Wordsworth's most famous poems: *Lines Written A Few Miles Above Tintern Abbey, On Revisiting the Banks of the Wye During a Tour, July 13, 1798*. The poem's explicit choice of date and its reference to the passage of five years recall events in France on July 13th 1793 when the revolutionary politician Marat was murdered in his bath. By placing himself on the banks of the River Wye at this time, Wordsworth – whether consciously or not – distanced himself from the period of amatory and political experimentation which had characterised his time in France. Upon his return from Germany in 1799, he settled in the Lake District with his sister and later married his childhood friend, Mary Hutchinson, with whom he had five children. (He also found means to bestow funds upon his love-child with Annette Vallon.) After years of stubborn endeavour, his poetry finally earned critical acclaim and in 1843 he was appointed Poet Laureate upon the death of Southey.

Select Bibliography

The Life of Samuel Taylor Coleridge, Rosemary Ashton (1996)

Wordsworth: A Life, Juliet Barker (2000)

British Society & the French Wars 1793-1815, Clive Emsley (1979)

The Hanging Tree: Execution and the English People 1770-1868, VAC Gatrell (1994)

William Pitt the Younger, William Hague (2004)

The Unfortunate Colonel Despard, Mike Jay (2004)

Coleridge and Wordsworth in the West Country, Tom Mayberry (1992)

Wordsworth and Coleridge: The Radical Years, Nicolas Roe (1988)

Britain's Last Invasion: Fishguard 1797, JE Thomas (2007)

The Man Who Broke Napoleon's Codes, Mark Urban (2001)

Coleridge the Poet, George Watson (1966)

The Duke of Portland: Politics and Party in the Age of George III, David Wilkinson (2003)

Acknowledgements

First and foremost, thank you to Hannah for her great interest in and encouragement of this project since its inception. No dedication, however elaborately worded, could do this full justice.

Thanks also to my friends at the Rose & Crown Group; to Giles, Maartje and Sarah; and to my family – particularly my father for accompanying me on a memorable expedition along the Coleridge Way and my mother for providing us with vital logistical support.

I am grateful to the helpful staff at Somerset Heritage Centre in Taunton; to Iwan ap Dafydd at the National Library of Wales; and to Duncan and Clare at York Publishing Services.

Finally, I wish to thank everyone who has demonstrated support for my writing over the years. It really is very greatly appreciated.

About the Author

Matthew Greenwood took a Double First in English at Pembroke College, Cambridge, and an MA in Victorian Studies at the University of Leicester. His first novel, *A Rabbit Named Gunther*, was published in 2010.